AMATEUR RADIO EMERGENCY COMMUNICATIONS COURSE

LEVEL I

2nd Edition [A]

Copyright @ 2003 American Radio Relay League, Inc.   ISBN: 0-87259-846-2

Table of Contents

Amateur radio Emergency Communications is provided by several different types of emergency communications organizations. Level I, II and III courses have addressed some of these groups specifically. Examples are ARES, RACES, ACS, SKYWARN, SATERN, REACT, etc.

It is not the intent of this series of courses to promote any specific group over another. The Amateur Radio Emergency Service (ARES) sponsored by the American Radio Relay League has the longest history of public service of any Amateur Radio emergency communications provider organizations. It is also the largest group and is found in almost every sector of the country. Many other groups are not. Therefore, specific knowledge of the ARES organizational structure and the duties and responsibilities of key ARES positions is important. Those matters will be discussed in detail in the Level III course.

ARRL AREC Courses are specifically intended to provide more emergency communications tools to be used as may be appropriate for any given area. What works well fighting forest fires in Colorado may not work in conjunction with flooding in Pennsylvania. Use this information to benefit your community by adding whatever fits your particular area needs. Local protocol and training always takes precedence.

On behalf of all the volunteer efforts to put these courses together, thanks for your participation.

Amateur Radio Emergency Communications Course (ARECC) Contributors

The following people/groups have been instrumental in providing valuable assistance to the program. This is by no means a complete list of contributors. We've gratefully received too many to name them all. Whether all or part of their material was used in the actual course, or if we simply used their material as review or reference in what was needed to be covered, we are sincerely grateful to each and every one for their dedication and willingness to participate. Only with their help, have we been able to complete the best ARRL training tool for Emergency Communications that has ever been put together.

Thanks to everyone who assisted!

ARECC Advisory Committee
Second Edition Editor: Dave Colter, WA1ZCN

L.B. Cebik, W4RNL
Dan Miller, K3UFG
Rick Palm, K1CE
Pat Lambert, W0IPL
Ron Hashiro, AH6RH
Gary Payne N9VE
Greg Jones K3GJ
David Doane KC6YSO
Joe Dorn W5VEX
Paul Cavnar NN7B
Jack Riegel III N5JAK
Lyle Meek W6WF
Betsey Doane K1EIC
Terry Dettman WX7S
David Lane KG4GIY

Harry Lewis W7JWJ
Rich Slover, ND4F
Rob Foshay, W9VK
Eldon McDonald, KE4OCW
Taylor Davidson, N4TD
Jeff Stidham, KC7FUY
Richard Werner, K7UK
Ed Harris, KE4SKY
Randy Long, W0AVV
Dave Tuttle, NC4DT
Tuck Miller, NZ6T
Stan Kaplan, WB9RQR
Jim Cluett, W1PID
Jerry Boyd, K6BZ

ARECC Contributors

Please note that the names and calls are in alphabetic call suffix sequence.

Patrick Taber, W5ABQ
Terry Busby, W5ARS
Art Feller, W4ART
Perry Lundquist, W6AUN
Randy Allen, KA0AZS
Paul Cavnar, NN7B
Kelly Bersch, KC7CSB
Mark Jewell, KC6CUB
Ben Green, WD8CZP

Margie Bourgoin, KB1DCO
Brian Fernandez, KE6HKJ
Tom McClain, N3HPR
Larry Dunn, N9HSW
Randall Winchester, WD4HVA
Mary Lau, N7IAL
Ken Akasofu, KL7JCQ
Mark Greene, PhD KD7JNF
Scott Garrett, W8JSG

Dave Waltrous, WD2K
John Hennessee, N1KB
Max Soucia, N1KQS
Fred Stone, W8LLY
Ray Moody, AH6LT
Suzy Price, N2LZR
Dave Patton, NT1N
Ruben Kafenbaum, WA2NBL
Jim Andrews, WA0NHD
Nick Leggett, N3NL
F. Dale Williams, K3PUR
Dennis Bodson, W4PWF
Bob Josuweit, WA3PZO
John Evans, N2QCE
Brennan Price, N4QX

Len Koppl, KD0RC
T.S. Bell, N2RSI
Ken Goetz, N2SQW
Rosalie White, K1STO
Paul Drothler, WO4U
Robert Lunsford, KB8UEY
Rich Werner K7UK
Peter Laws, N5UWY
Mike Manes, W5VSI
Jim Weslager, K3WR
Steve Ewald, WV1X
Ed Bixby, AK0X
David Doane KC6YSO
Dave Colter WA1ZCN

Organizations that we have received input from.
(Please note that the names are in alphabetic sequence.)

Colorado Section ARES
Erie County, PA, SKYWARN
Fairfax County, VA, RACES

ARECC Level I – Introduction to Amateur Radio Emergency Communications

OBJECTIVES:

To provide a baseline level of knowledge and skill in Amateur Radio Emergency Communications for anyone wishing to assist their local emergency communications organizations.

COURSE DESCRIPTION:

This is the first of the ARRL courses in Amateur Radio emergency communications. Regardless of prior experiences and knowledge, this course is designed to prepare volunteers for participation with their local emergency communications organization.

All ARRL Amateur Radio Emergency Communications Courses are intended for use in conjunction with local protocol and training already available. These courses have been developed using material from all over our great country. This general knowledge is intended to provide additional tools for your use. These courses are a method for raising emergency communications awareness regardless of geographic location.

TARGETED AUDIENCE:

Volunteer Amateur Radio operators wishing to be more involved in emergency communications at an introductory level.

Gender references in this course:
The writers and editors of this and every AREC course have struggled long and hard to find a workable solution to the issue of gender reference. With all due respect, please accept all male and/or female references as inclusive of both genders anywhere this is appropriate in context.

PREREQUISITES:

A desire to raise personal skill level and gain additional knowledge of Amateur Radio emergency communications. An HF license and HF equipment is highly recommended.

Learning Unit 1

Introduction to Emergency Communication

Objectives:

This unit will introduce you to the general concepts of emergency communication and how you, as volunteers, can best help.

Student preparation required:

You should have a sincere interest in improving your skills as an emergency communication volunteer.

Information:

Welcome!

As you begin this series of courses, let us first thank you for choosing to expand your knowledge of Amateur Radio emergency communication, or "emcomm" as it is often called. Our professionalism and the effectiveness of our public service efforts will be greatly improved if we all share a common base of knowledge, skills, and procedures.

In this course, you will learn new skills, and new ways of thinking about existing skills. Sometimes the way we have always done something is no longer useful or appropriate. We hope that this course will challenge you to become the best emergency communicator possible.

You may have ideas and material that could add to the base of knowledge presented here. Do not send these comments to your mentor as you take the course. Simply make a note of them and include them in the course evaluation form you will fill out at the end of the course. Since our methods and techniques must continually change to meet the needs of the communities we serve, so must this course. The ARECC curriculum committee will make changes after making a careful periodic review of the course, and all student and mentor comments. A refresher course including these changes and other material will eventually be offered to keep everyone up-to-date.

What is a Communication Emergency?

A communication emergency exists when a critical communication system failure puts the public at risk. A variety of circumstances can overload or damage critical day-to-day communication systems. It could be a storm that knocks down telephone lines or radio towers, a massive increase in the use of a communication system that causes it to become overloaded, or the failure of a key component in a system that has widespread consequences.

Examples are easily found. Violent storms and earthquakes can knock down communication facilities. Critical facilities can also be damaged in "normal" circumstances: underground cables are dug up, fires occur in telephone equipment buildings, or a car crash knocks down a key telephone pole. Hospital or 911 telephone systems can fail. Even when no equipment fails, a large-scale emergency such as a chemical or nuclear accident can result in more message traffic than the system was designed to handle. Some emergency operations can occur in areas without any existing communication systems, such as with backcountry searches or fires.

What makes a good emcomm volunteer?

Emcomm volunteers come from a wide variety of backgrounds and with a range of skills and experience. The common attributes that all effective volunteers share are a desire to help others without personal gain of any kind, the ability to work as a member of a team, and to take direction from others. Emcomm volunteers need to be able to think and act quickly, under the stress and pressure of an emergency.

How do you fit in?

Amateur Radio operators have been a communication resource in emergency situations ever since there has been radio. Someone once described hams as "communication commandos." To the agencies you serve, you are their immediately available communication experts.

Amateurs have the equipment, the skills, and the frequencies necessary to create expedient emergency communication networks under poor conditions. They are licensed and pre-authorized for national and international communication. Hams have the ability to rapidly enlarge their communication capacity to meet growing needs in an emergency, something commercial and public safety systems cannot do. Many of the skills are the same ones you use in everyday ham activities.

However, just having radios, frequencies, and basic radio skills is not enough. Certain emergency communication skills are very different from those you use in your daily ham radio life. Courses like this one help fill that need, as do local training programs and regular emergency exercises. Without specific emergency communication skills, you can easily become part of the problem rather than part of the solution.

As you might expect, technical and operating skills are critical. Just as important, though, is your ability to function as a team player within your own organization, and the organization you are serving. Those critical skills will also be covered in this course.

What you are not

As important as what you are, is what you are not. There are limits to your responsibilities as an emergency communicator, and it is important to know where to draw the line.

You are not a "first responder." Except in rare cases of serendipity, you will seldom be first on the scene. You do not need flashing lights and sirens, gold badges, or fancy uniforms. In most cases, beyond reporting the situation to the proper authorities, hams have little usefulness as communicators at the onset of an emergency.

You have no authority. In most cases, you cannot make decisions for others, or make demands on the agency you serve or any other agency. The only decisions you can make are whether to participate or not, and those affecting your own health and safety.

You cannot do it all. When the agency you are helping runs short of doctors, cooks, or traffic cops, it is not your job to fill the void. In most cases, you are not trained for it. That does mean you can lend a hand to fill an urgent need *when you are qualified to do so*, or perform other jobs for the served agency *of which communication is an integral part*, and for which you are trained and capable.

You are not in charge. You are there to temporarily fulfill the needs of an agency whose communication system is unable to do its job. They tell you what they need, and you do your best to comply.

"Day-to-Day" Versus "Emergency" Communication

In your daily ham radio life, there is no pressure to get any particular message through. You do things at your leisure, and no one's life depends upon you. In an emergency all that changes. Here are some differences you may see:

- Unlike general Amateur Radio activities, which involve primarily Amateur Radio operators, emergency communication involves both amateurs and non-amateurs.

- Unlike regular activities, emergency operations happen in real time. Important activities cannot be delayed for convenience.

- Instead of one leisurely net a day, emergency communicators are often dealing with several continuous nets simultaneously to pass critical messages within a limited timeframe.

- Unlike public service events that are scheduled and planned, emergency communicators are often asked to organize and coordinate field operations with little or no warning.

- Unlike public service events where the communicators serve primarily under the direction of one lead organization, emergency communicators may need to interact with several key organizations simultaneously.

- Unlike typical home installations, emergency stations must be portable and able to be set up and operational anywhere in a very short time.

- Unlike contesting, which involves contacting any station for points, emergency communicators need to contact specific stations quickly to pass important messages. Teamwork is important, not competition between stations.

- Unlike Field Day, where you can plan on a two-day operation, emergency operations have no schedule and are likely to continue for at least several days.

- Unlike commercial communication solutions, where there is no reserve capacity for handling a sudden and massive increase in communication volume, Amateur Radio emergency communicators have the equipment, skills, and knowledge to create additional capacity in a very short time.

The Missions

The job you are asked to do will vary with the specific agency you serve. If that agency is the American Red Cross, you will be providing the communications needed to maintain a system of shelters and other relief efforts. If it is a state or local emergency management agency, you could be handling interagency communications, or serving as the eyes and ears of the emergency managers. When a hospital's telephone system fails, you might be handling the "mechanics" of communicating so that doctors and nurses can concentrate on patients. In a large forest-fire or search and rescue operation, you might be setting up personal phone patches for firefighters or rescuers to their families, or assisting with logistical communications to insure that food, supplies, personnel and materials arrive when and where needed. For the National Weather Service you will be reporting storm locations and weather conditions so that they can better inform and warn the public. In any widespread disaster, hams could be assisting all the agencies listed above, and more.

Communicating – Job #1

While you are proud of your skill as a radio operator, and the impressive equipment and systems you have in place, it is important to remember that your job is "communicating." If an agency asks us to deliver a long shelter supply list to headquarters, you should be prepared to use any means required – including the fax machine if it is still working.

Our job is to get the message through, even if it means using smoke signals. Do not think about how to use ham radio to send the message – just think about the best and fastest way to send it. If that means using ham radio, so much the better. If all you have is CB or Family Radio, use it. If an agency asks you to use their radio system, do it. Your operating and technical skills are just as important as your ham radio resources.

Anatomy of a communication emergency

In the earliest phases of many disasters, there is no immediate need for emergency communication services. (An obvious exception would be a tornado or earthquake.) This phase might occur during a severe storm "watch" or "warning" period. You should use this time to monitor developments and prepare to deploy when and if a request for assistance comes. Some nets, such as the Hurricane Watch Net or SKYWARN, may be activated early in the storm watch or warning phases to provide the National Weather Service and other agencies with up-to-the-minute information.

Once a potential or actual need for more communication resources is identified, a served agency puts out the call for its volunteer communicators. Depending on the situation, operators and equipment might be needed at an Emergency Operations Center (EOC) or to set up in field locations, or both.

In some areas, a "Rapid Response Team" (RRT) or similar small sub-group might deploy a minimal response in a very short time, to be backed up by a second, more robust response in an hour or two.

A "resource" or "logistics" net might be set up to handle incoming communication volunteers and direct resources where they are needed most. Any volunteer not presently assigned to a specific net or task should check into and monitor this net.

Once operations begin, all kinds of things can happen. The volume of messages can grow quickly, and confusion is common. In addition to handling messages, your organization will need to think about relief or replacement operators, food and water, sleeping accommodations, batteries, fuel, and other logistical needs. Radios and antennas will fail and need to be replaced. Some operators will need to leave early for personal reasons.

Communication assignments might include staffing a shelter to handle calls for information, supplies, and personnel, "shadowing" an official to be their communication link, gathering weather information, or collecting and transmitting damage reports. Some nets might pass health and welfare inquiries to refugee centers, or pass messages from refugees to family members outside the disaster area. Other nets might handle logistical needs for the served agency, such as those regarding supplies, equipment, and personnel.

Nets will be set up, re-arranged, and dismantled as needs change. Volunteers will need to remain flexible in order to meet the changing needs of the served agency. Over time, the need for emergency communication networks will diminish as the message load decreases, and some nets will be closed or reduced in size. Operators will be released to go home one by one, in small groups, or all at once as the needs dictate.

Not long after the operation has ended, the emergency communication group should review the effectiveness of its response, either alone or with the served agency. This might be done on the air in a formal net, by email, or in a face-to-face meeting. However it is done, it should occur as soon as possible after operations have ended to be sure that events are fresh in everyone's mind. Critiques, done properly, can greatly improve your organization's – and your own – effectiveness.

Reference links:

ARRL Public Service Communication Manual

Review:

Communication emergencies can result from a variety of situations, including storms, earthquakes, fires, and equipment damage or failure. Normal communication systems are rapidly overloaded by the increase in usage caused by an emergency, and most have little or no reserve capacity.
Amateur Radio operators are a national resource in a communication emergency, and your mission will vary with the agency you serve. Hams have the skills, equipment, and frequencies to rapidly expand the message carrying capacity of their networks. Specific emcomm skills are also required to meet the special needs of a communication emergency.

Student activities:

1a. List **three** ways in which Emergency Communications are **similar** to Non-emergency Communications.

1b. List **six** ways in which Emergency Communications **differ** from Non-emergency Communications.

2. In an emergency situation, a served agency asks you to forward an urgent message. Which one of the following methods would you NOT employ? In one or two sentences, tell why you selected your answer.
a. CB radio
b. Family radio
c. Informal, conversational grapevine
d. The served agency's own radio system.

Share your responses to both activities with your mentor.

Questions:
.

1. When does a communication emergency exist?
A. Whenever the public is at risk.
B. When there is an earthquake in your area and the public is inconvenienced.
C. When a critical communication system fails and the public is inconvenienced.
D. When a critical communication system fails and the public is put at risk.

2. Which of the following is it most important for an emcomm group to do at the end of an emergency communication operation?
A. Review the effectiveness of its response.
B. Take photos of the activity.
C. Call the local newspaper to schedule interviews
D. Review the activities of the first responders.

3. Which of the following is NOT a responsibility of emergency communicators?
A. Making demands on the agency being served.
B. Having radios, frequencies and basic radio skills.
C. Being licensed and preauthorized for national and international communications.
D. Possessing emergency communication skills.

4. Which of the following describes the function of a Rapid Response Team (RRT)?
A. To handle large-scale emergencies over an extended period.
B. To deploy a quick response in a very short time.
C. To establish and operate a storm watch prior to any emergency.
D. To review the effectiveness of an emergency communication group.

5. In an emergency situation -- when a served agency asks you to forward an urgent message -- which one of the following methods would you NOT employ?
A. CB radio
B. Family radio
C. Informal, conversational grapevine
D. The served agency's own radio system.

Learning Unit 2

Amateurs As Professionals – The Served Agency Relationship

Objective:

This unit will help you to understand the critical and delicate relationship between emergency communicators and the agencies they serve.

Student preparation required:

None

Information:

What has my "attitude" got to do with this?

In a word, everything! It is even more important than your radio skills. Historically speaking, the attitude of some Amateur Radio volunteers has been our weakest point.

In situations where a professional and helpful attitude is maintained, served agencies point with pride to ham's efforts and accomplishments. The opposite situation is clearly illustrated in the words of one emergency management official who said, "Working with ham radio operators is like herding cats – get them the heck out of here!" This man was clearly frustrated with the attitude of his volunteers.

Although our name says that we are "Amateurs," its real reference is to the fact that we are not paid for our efforts. It need not imply that our efforts or demeanor will be anything less than professional. "Professionalism" means getting the job done efficiently – with a minimum of fuss.

No matter which agency you serve – emergency management, the Red Cross, or others, it is helpful to remember that emcomm volunteers are like unpaid employees. If you maintain the attitude that you are an employee of the agency you are serving, with all that employee status implies, there is little chance for you to go astray. You are there to help solve their communication problems. Do whatever you can, within reason, to accomplish that goal, and avoid becoming part of the problem.

Who Works For Whom

The relationship between the volunteer communicator and served agency will vary somewhat from situation to situation, but the fact is that *you work for them*. It doesn't matter whether you are part of a separate radio group like ARES, or part of the agency's regular volunteer force. *You* still work for *them*.

Your job as a communicator is to meet the needs of the served agency. Period. It is not to show off your fancy equipment, nor to impress anyone with your knowledge of radio and electronics. A "know-it-all" or "I will show you how good I am, and how inadequate you are" attitude will end your – and our -- relationship with the served agency in a hurry.

It is often said that volunteers don't have to take orders. This is true – we do not. However, when you volunteer your services to an organization, you implicitly agree to accept and comply with reasonable orders and requests from your "employer." If you do not feel comfortable doing this, do not volunteer.

There may be times that you find yourself unwilling or unable to comply with a served agency's demands. The reasons may be personal, or related to safety or health, or it may be that you do not consider yourself qualified or capable of meeting a particular demand. On rare occasions, it may be that they ask you to do something not permitted by FCC rules. Regardless of the reason, respectfully explain the situation, and work with the served agency or your superiors in the communication group to come up with an alternative solution. If the discussion with the served agency becomes difficult or uncomfortable, you can always politely pass the discussion up to your immediate emcomm superiors so that they can handle it instead.

How Professional Emergency Responders Often View Volunteers

Unless a positive and long established relationship exists between professionals and volunteers, professionals who do not work regularly with competent volunteers are likely to look at them as "less than useful." There are several reasons for this. Fire departments have a long history of competitive relationships between professional and volunteer firefighters, and this attitude may carry over to volunteers in general. Police agencies are often distrustful of outsiders – often for legitimate information security concerns. Professionals in any field put a great deal of time and effort into their skills and training, and take considerable pride in their professional standing. As a result, they may view themselves as able to handle all possible situations without outside assistance.

Volunteers, on the other hand, are often viewed as "part timers" whose skill level and dedication to the job vary widely. Many agencies and organizations have learned that some volunteers cannot be depended on when they are needed most. Do not be offended if this attitude is obvious, and remember that you cannot change it overnight. It takes time for you to prove yourselves, and for a positive working relationship to develop and mature.

The middle of an on-going incident is not the time to try to change a "we do not need you" attitude. If your offer of assistance is refused, do not press the issue. The incident commander is busy with more pressing needs, and if he changes his mind about your offer, he will probably contact you. Remember: the incident commander's authority should never be challenged – he is in charge, and you are not.

Performing Non-Communication Roles

It has been said many times that our job should be strictly limited to communication. But is this a hard and fast rule? When you work as a SKYWARN weather spotter, or collect and relay damage reports for the Red Cross, is this not going beyond your role as a communicator?

Well, yes and no. The old model of the emergency communicator was one where a written message would be generated by the served agency and handed to the radio operator. They would format and transmit the message to another station, whose operator would then write it out and then deliver it to the addressee. In this role, hams were strictly communicators, and due to the radio technology of the times, it was appropriate. Those days are gone forever.

In today's fast paced emergency responses, there is often no time for this sort of system. Events are happening too quickly, and the agency's communications must move at the same speed. The job description will more likely be "any function that also *includes* communication," as defined by the served agency. For this reason, emergency communication groups should engage in pre-planning with the served agency to ensure that these jobs are clearly defined, and any additional job-specific training required is obtained in advance.

In general, emcomm groups should be prepared to perform jobs for their served agency that include the need to communicate. Here are a few of the many possible job descriptions:
- Radio operator, using amateur or served agency radio systems.
- Dispatcher, organizing the flow of personnel, vehicles, and supplies.
- Resource coordinator, organizing the assignments of disaster relief volunteers.
- Field observer, watching and reporting weather or other conditions.
- Damage assessor, evaluating and reporting damage conditions.
- Van driver, moving people or supplies from location to location.
- Searcher, also providing communication for a search and rescue team.

To perform these jobs, you may need to complete task-specific training courses, and take part in exercises and drills in addition to those required for emergency communication even beyond traditional Amateur Radio. In the ever-changing world of emergency response, this flexibility will become increasingly important if we are to continue our contribution to public safety as Amateur Radio operators.

Note:

Some emcomm groups may still enforce a "communication only" policy, and in some agencies, the old model may still be appropriate. Discuss this with your Emergency Coordinator or similar emcomm manager to be sure.

Specific Agency Relationships

The relationship between the volunteer communicator and the served agency can be quite different from agency to agency, and even between different offices of the same agency. While the ARRL and other national communication groups have existing "Memorandums of Understanding" (MOUs) in place with many served agencies that define our general relationships, the actual working relationship is more precisely defined a the local level. Different people have different ideas and management styles, agencies in one area can have different needs from others, and these can affect the working relationship between the agency and its emcomm volunteers. Here are some examples of those relationships:

- *Federal Emergency Management Agency (FEMA) and Federal Agencies*: In most cases you will have little direct contact with federal agencies, except within the Military Affiliate Radio System (MARS) and at the national level with ARRL.
- *American Red Cross* chapters may have their own communication teams that include Amateurs, or they may have a MOU with a local ARES group or radio club. Typical assignments include linking shelters and chapter houses, performing damage assessment, and handling supply and personnel logistics.
- *The Salvation Army* maintains its own internal Amateur Radio communication support group, known as the Salvation Army Team Emergency Radio Network (SATERN). In some areas, ARES or other groups provide local communication support. Assignments are similar to the Red Cross.
- *State and Local Emergency Management:* Some state and local emergency management agencies include Radio Amateur Civil Emergency Service (RACES) teams as part of their own emergency communication plan. Others use "outside" groups such as the Amateur Radio Emergency Service (ARES). In a growing trend around the country, all ARES members are also RACES registered operators and vice versa. Communication assignments may be similar to the Red Cross and Salvation Army, but may also include government command and control, and inter-agency communications.
- *SKYWARN* is a self-contained program sponsored by the National Weather Service, and not all members are Amateur Radio operators. Many use other radio systems or telephone, fax or email to send in weather observations. SKYWARN volunteers collect on the spot weather observations that will allow forecasters to create forecasts that are more accurate, and issue timely warnings.

Talking to the Press

In an emergency situation, the press will be hunting for any tidbit of information they can get, and they may not care where they get it. One place they should *never* get information regarding the served agency or its efforts is from *you*. Politely refer all such inquiries to the served agency's public spokesperson. If you offer such information "just to be helpful," because you enjoy "being in the spotlight," or to get some publicity for yourself or your emcomm group, the served agency would be well within its rights to ask you to leave.

Some emcomm organizations also have their own spokesperson. In ARES this person is called the "Public Information Officer" (PIO) – other organizations may use a different job title. Their job is to handle press inquiries so those radio operators can do their jobs without interruption. In most cases, they would only answer questions about the Amateur Radio group's efforts, and not those of the served agency.

If a reporter just will not leave you alone, you might feel obliged to say something so they will go away. In this case, the only thing you should discuss is your part of the emergency communication effort, but only if you are part of a separate emcomm group such as ARES, and *only if that organization's policy permits it*. If they are impeding your ability to do your job, briefly explain this to the reporter and politely but firmly direct them to the PIO or an emcomm management person.

Regardless of the situation, it is always a good policy to know in advance how your organization or served agency would like you to deal with press inquiries. If your emcomm organization does not have a "press" policy, you might suggest that one be developed. This will help prevent misunderstandings and hard feelings later.

Volunteering Where You Are Not Known

In some cases, an emergency occurs in a neighboring area where you are not a member of the responding communication group. For whatever reason, you might feel obligated to offer your services. If at all feasible, it is best to make your offer before making any significant preparations, or leaving home.

It is possible that your offer might be welcomed, but is equally possible that it will be refused. There are good reasons for this, particularly where the served agency has specific requirements, such as specialized training, official IDs, and time consuming background checks. Most emcomm managers prefer to work only with operators whose abilities and limitations they know. They may also have more volunteers than they need, or may feel that your skills or equipment are not suited to their mission. If you are turned away, please accept the situation gracefully.

On the other hand, if your offer of assistance is accepted, the situation you find may vary quite a bit. In a well-organized effort, there will be someone to help orient you to the response effort, provide any required information, and answer your questions. Your assignment will be clear, a relief person will be sent along at the end of a pre-defined shift, and you will know of any arrangements for food, sanitation, and sleep.

If the effort is not well organized, little, if any, of the above scenario could be true. You might be given an assignment, but with little additional information or support. In this case, you will need to improvise and fend for yourself, and you should be prepared to do so. This is one good reason for making your offer of assistance in advance. Learn as much as you can about the response before preparing to leave home.

In any event, the best time to offer your services to an emcomm group is well before any emergency occurs. This will allow you to obtain the proper training and credentials, and to become known to the group's managers. When the time comes to serve, you will be ready for your job, and a job ready for you.

Worker's Compensation Coverage and Legal Protections

In some states, Worker's Compensation insurance coverage can be extended to volunteers working on behalf of a government or non-profit agency. However, Worker's Compensation law is a rather complex matter regulated by individual state's laws. In many cases, it may not be possible for volunteers who are not also paid employees of a served agency to be covered by Worker's Compensation. Emcomm managers should investigate their state's laws on this subject rather than assume that the agency's Worker's Compensation coverage will automatically apply.

Volunteers providing services to government agencies or Section 501(c)(3) tax-exempt private organizations are provided immunity from liability by Federal law through the Volunteer Protection Act of 1997, 42 U.S.C. Section 14501. This generally limits liability if the volunteer was acting at the time within the scope of official duties under a volunteer program. There are exceptions: the law does not cover volunteers who cause harm while operating motor vehicles, or if the volunteer is grossly negligent, or engages in criminal acts. The statute, however, provides broad liability protection for Amateurs in most contexts, and especially where Amateurs volunteer under ARES to provide emergency communications to served agencies.

Reference links:

American Red Cross - www.redcross.org
Salvation Army - www.salvationarmy.org
SKYWARN - www.SKYWARN.org
Army Military Affiliate Radio Service (MARS) - www.asc.army.mil/mars/default.htm
Federal Emergency Management Agency - www.fema.gov
ARRL MOUs with various agencies - www.arrl.org/Fand ES/field/mou/index.html
ARRL Public Service Communications Manual – Served Agencies

Review:

The relationship between Amateur Radio operators and a served agency is a critical one. Emcomm volunteers should maintain a professional attitude at all times and remember that their relationship to the served agency is much like that of an employee – without the paycheck. Agency relationships will vary with the agency, region, and the needs and style of local management.

Avoid giving any information to the press until you understand both the served agency's and your own emcomm group's policies on speaking to the press. Most groups will want all information to come from a central official source, such as a "public information officer."

When volunteering where you are not known, do not be surprised if your offer is refused. Emcomm groups often have requirements that cannot be met during an actual emergency.

Student activities:

1. Locate the ARRL website. Conduct a search for the Statement of Understanding (SOU) between The American Red Cross and ARRL. Based on the SOU, what three forms of assistance may the Red Cross request of ARRL ARES and NTS?

2. If you were asked to develop a Statement of Understanding (MOU) between your local emcomm group and a local served agency, what general **topics** would you include?

Questions:

*1. Which of the following best describes your **main job** as an emergency communicator?*
A. Dispatcher, organizing the flow of vehicles, personnel, and supplies.
B. Meeting the needs of the served agency.
C. Radio operator, using Amateur or served agency radio systems.
D. Resource coordinator, organizing the assignments of disaster relief volunteers.

*2. Which of the following best describes the **role** of a modern emergency communicator?*
A. You are strictly limited to communication tasks.
B. You may be asked to serve any function that includes communication.
C. You do anything a served agency asks.
D. You transmit and receive messages.

3. If you are asked by a served agency to perform a task that falls outside FCC rules, which of the following is a proper response?
A. Document the request, and then do what is asked.
B. Document the request, but refuse to do it.
C. Leave immediately.
D. Discuss the situation with the served agency, and develop an alternative solution.

4. In an emergency situation, which of the following is the most appropriate response that you as an emcomm group member can make to an inquiry from the press?
A. Answer any question that you are asked.
B. Volunteer information and make yourself helpful to them.
C. Refer all inquiries to the served agency's public information officer (PIO).
D. Ignore them and hope they will go away.

4. *In an emergency situation, which of the following is the most appropriate response that you as an emcomm group member can make to an inquiry from the press?*
A. Answer any question that you are asked.
B. Volunteer information and make yourself helpful to them.
C. Refer all inquiries to the served agency's public information officer (PIO).
D. Ignore them and hope they will go away.

5. *Which of the following will most affect your relationship with a served agency?*
A. Your radio and electronic equipment.
B. Your knowledge of FCC regulations.
C. Your attitude.
D. Your radio skills.

Learning Unit 3

Emergency Communication Organizations & Systems

Objective: Emergency communication organizations are what make an emcomm response possible. This unit introduces several of the largest and best-known organizations, and a number of related emcomm and public warning systems.

Student preparation required:

None

Information:

Why is organization so important to emcomm?

Imagine a random group of volunteers trying to tackle a full-scale disaster communication emergency, working together for the first time. They do not know each other well, have very different approaches to solving the same problem, and half of them want to be in charge. Get the picture?

It is not too far-fetched. Just ask anyone who has been around emcomm for a while – they have seen it! This course is intended to help solve that problem, but without emcomm organizations, this course would be worthless.

Emcomm organizations provide training, and a forum to share ideas and develop workable solutions to problems in advance of a real disaster. This way, when the time comes to assist the served agency, you will be as prepared as you can be. The response will occur more smoothly, challenges will be dealt with productively, and the served agency's needs met.

Some of the organizations listed here do not directly involve Amateur Radio operators, but knowing about them and how they might assist in an emergency may be helpful. Your served agency may utilize or interact with one or more of these systems or organizations.

Amateur Radio Emergency Service (ARES)

Among the largest and oldest emcomm groups is ARES, a program sponsored by the American Radio Relay League (ARRL) since 1935. ARES is part of the League's field organization, which is composed of "Sections". Most Sections are entire states, but some larger states have two or more Sections.

The elected Section Manager (SM) appoints top ARES leadership. The top ARES leader in each section is the Section Emergency Coordinator (SEC).

Some larger Sections, like Wisconsin, Michigan, and Florida, are further divided into two or more Districts. In this case, each District is guided by a District Emergency Coordinator (DEC), working directly under the SEC. (See diagram below.)

The next subdivision within ARES is the "county" or similar region assigned to an Emergency Coordinator (EC). Most ECs will have one or more Assistant Emergency Coordinators (AEC), who may have responsibility for specific tasks or cities. A large city with complex needs may have its own EC.

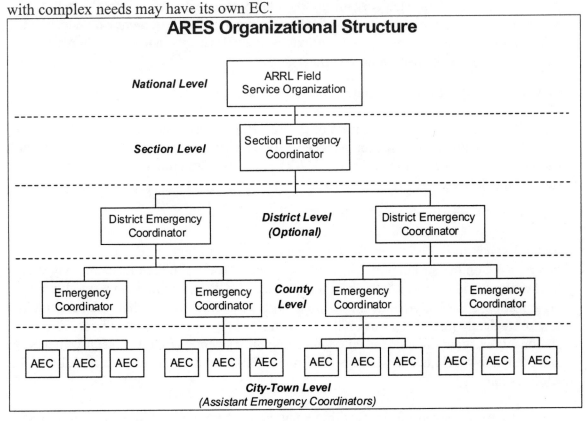

ARES Organizational Structure

ARES has Memoranda of Understanding (MOUs) with a variety of agencies at the national level, including the Federal Emergency Management Agency (FEMA), American Red Cross, Salvation Army, and the National Weather Service. These documents set out the general relationship between ARES and the agency at the national level, and provide guidance for local units of both organizations to draft more specific local MOUs.

In addition to local chapters of national groups, ARES groups often have MOUs or other written or verbal agreements with state and city emergency management departments, hospitals, schools, police and fire departments, public works agencies, and others.

Radio Amateur Civil Emergency Service (RACES)

The federal government created RACES after World War II. It addressed the need for a group of hams to operate as an integral part of the Civil Defense organization in time of national emergency or war. The RACES program also provides the means to continue to serve the public if the President suspends regular Amateur operations. The RACES rules provide for use of almost all regular Amateur frequencies, but place strict limits on the types of communications made, and with whom.

Over the years, both RACES and Civil Defense have changed dramatically. While the RACES rules are the same, there are fewer pure RACES groups today. More and more of them have become "dual-hat" organizations. This means that RACES members also belong to ARES, and can "switch hats" when the need arises. Emergency management officials like this arrangement since it provides more flexibility, and gives them more direct control over the ham radio volunteers.

Salvation Army Team Emergency Radio Network (SATERN)

SATERN members are also members of the Salvation Army. Their HF networks are used for both logistical communication between various Salvation Army offices and for health and welfare messages. At the local level, ARES, REACT and other groups often help support the Salvation Army's operations.

The "Rapid Response Team" (RRT)

In the first minutes of an emergency, it is sometimes important to get the basic essentials of a network on the air quickly. The solution is the "RRT", although its name may vary. In Hawaii, it is known as a "Quick Response Team" (QRT). Rather than a stand-alone organization, a RRT is small team within a larger emcomm group. Their job is to put a few strategically placed stations on the air within the first half-hour to an hour. These stations will usually include the emergency operations center (EOC), a resource net NCS, and often a few field teams where needed most. This is commonly known as a "Level 1 RRT response".

A Level 2 RRT response follows within a few hours, bringing additional resources and operators. Level 1 teams have pre-assigned jobs, and short-term (12-24 hour) "jump kits", ready to go whenever the call comes. Level 2 teams have longer term (72 hour) jump kits, and a variety of other equipment, possibly including tents, portable repeaters, food and water supplies, sleeping gear, spare radios, and generators, depending on local needs.

ARES Mutual Assistance Team (ARESMAT)

When a communication emergency lasts longer than a day or two, or when the scale of the emergency is beyond the ability of a local ARES group to handle, help can be requested from neighboring areas. The ARESMAT concept was created to meet that need. These teams consist of hams who are willing and able to travel to another area for a period to assist ARES groups based in the disaster area. They may also bring additional resources in the form of radios, antennas, and other critical equipment. If you travel to another area as part of an ARESMAT, remember that the local group is still in charge – you are there to do what they need done. In a sense, they become another "served agency".

Military Affiliate Radio Service (MARS)

MARS is a <u>Department of Defense</u> sponsored auxiliary communication program, established as three separately managed and operated programs by the <u>Army</u>, <u>Navy</u>, and <u>Air Force</u>. The program enlists the services of licensed hams who operate disciplined and structured nets on assigned military radio frequencies adjacent to the Amateur bands. MARS has a strict set of rules regarding the type, content and format of messages. Special call signs are issued for MARS use.

In day-to-day service, MARS stations handle quasi-official and morale messages for the three services. During times of emergency, MARS provides backup communication networks to military, federal, state, and local agencies. MARS' most visible mission, providing phone patches to family members for US military personnel overseas, has diminished with the advent of new satellites that provide email and phone service almost anywhere. However, this has never been MARS largest or most important function. One advantage of the MARS system is that it is specifically authorized to communicate with other government radio services in time of emergency, including the federal SHARES HF networks.

National Traffic System (NTS)

Long before e-mail and the Internet, there was ARRL's NTS. The concept on which NTS is based is as old as ARRL itself. The NTS consists of local, regional and national nets operating on a regular basis to pass messages (traffic) from place to place. In day-to-day usage, the NTS handles non-critical organizational messages for its own members and ARRL field organizations, radiograms for the public, and various personal messages. Since e-mail has become popular, the NTS has seen a significant decrease in the number of messages passed through the system, and a corresponding decrease in membership and overall effectiveness. However, NTS still has an important role in emergency communication, and discussions about modernizing the NTS are underway. A more in depth discussion of NTS will follow later in this course.

Local Radio Clubs

Not every area has a working ARES or other nationally affiliated emcomm group. In many cases, the void is filled by local radio clubs who either work informally with served agencies, or with a formal MOU.

National Communications System (NCS)

A Federal agency, the NCS consists of 23 government organizations tasked with ensuring that the Federal Government has the necessary communication capabilities under all conditions from day-to-day use to national emergencies and international crises. These include the Forest Service, Federal Emergency Management Agency, Coast Guard, FBI, ATF, and others who have a variety of communication assets. The Manager of the NCS is also the Director of the Defense Information Systems Agency (DISA), usually an Air Force general.

SHARES

Even those who have been involved with emcomm for years may not know of the US Government's "Shared Resources System", known as "SHARES". This system is part of the NCS. It pairs certain MARS operators with various federal agencies and state emergency operations centers to provide a high frequency (HF) communication backbone if normal communication systems should fail. The SHARES system utilizes a number of nationwide and regional networks.

FEMA National Radio System (FNARS)

This is a FEMA high frequency (HF) radio network designed to provide a minimum essential emergency communication capability among Federal, State, local commonwealth, and territorial governments in times of national, natural and civil emergencies. FEMA monitors the FNARS HF frequencies on a daily basis.

Radio Emergency Associated Communications Teams (REACT)

REACT is another national emcomm group, whose members include Citizen's Band (CB) radio operators, hams, and others. In addition to CB and Amateur Radio, they may use General Mobile Radio Service (GMRS), Family Radio, and the Multiple Use Radio Service (MURS).

REACT has an organizational structure similar to ARRL/ARES, with local teams who directly serve many of the same agencies served by ARES and other ham radio emcomm groups. REACT has MOUs with many of these agencies, as well as with ARRL. REACT's mission is somewhat broader than that of ARES. They offer crowd and traffic control, logistics, public education, and other services that usually (but not always) include a need for radio communication.

Emergency Warning Systems

Emergency Alert System – EAS - (Broadcast Radio & TV):

The current EAS system has evolved from the earlier Emergency Broadcast System (EBS) and the original "CONELRAD System" developed during World War II. The EAS relies on radio and TV broadcast stations to relay emergency alert messages from federal, state, and local authorities. Messages may pertain to any immediate threat to public safety, including enemy attack, storm warnings, earthquake alerts, and wildfires. Messages are relayed from station to station using automatic switching systems and digital signaling. You may have heard the required weekly EAS tests performed by radio and TV stations and their distinctive digital "squawk" sound.

NOAA Weather Alert and National Weather Radio (NWR):

The National Weather Service (NWS) division of the National Oceanic and Atmospheric Administration (NOAA) operates NWR.

NWR uses seven frequencies in the 162MHz band to carry audio broadcasts to the public. Forecast and warning information originates from the regional network of forecasting offices, and yields timely and quality alerts dealing with weather and other natural events. Newer "weather alert" radios are available from a variety of manufacturers with the digital Specific Area Message Encoding (SAME) alert mechanism. SAME equipped radios will remain silent until an alert is received for a specific geographic area. The user programs one or more five-digit FIPS codes for the areas they wish to monitor. When the NWS broadcasts the alert with the SAME code matching that programmed into the receiver, the receiver will activate and allow you to hear the audio message concerning the alert. Some receivers also provide a textual display of the alert information. The NWS tests the SAME network at least once weekly, and the radio will indicate that it has heard the test alert within the past week.

NAWAS (National Warning System):

The federal government maintains a "hardened" and secure national wireline phone network connecting the warning points in each state. The center of NAWAS operations is the National Warning Center at NORAD's Cheyenne Mountain command and control complex in Colorado. Its primary purpose is to provide notification in case of enemy attack, and to inform and coordinate alert and warning information among states in a given region. During peacetime, it carries alerts on a variety of wide-ranging emergencies. Roll call check-ins are taken periodically during the day to ensure that the phone circuits are functioning properly.

Statewide Warning Systems:

These systems are similar to NAWAS, but at a state level. For most states that have such a system, county warning points are part of a statewide alert and warning network. It is known by different names in each state. For example, in Hawaii, it is HAWAS (Hawaii Warning System). In California, it is CALWAS.

In Hawaii, HAWAS connects the warning points in each island county, the Pacific Tsunami Warning Center, the local National Weather Service Forecast Office and the Hawaii Air National Guard's 199th Fighter (interceptor) Squadron, 154th Wing, stationed at Hickam Air Force Base. It keeps these key entities informed on a real-time basis of bulletins crucial to these agencies. The warning systems in other states are similar.

Tsunami Warning System:

A national and international network of warning points are connected together to provide timely exchange of tsunami warning information. In the United States, it is known as the Tsunami Warning System (TWS).

Information is relayed to a wide range of government, civil defense, military, and international tsunami research/warning points within each country or area.

National Earthquake Information Center (NEIC):

The U.S. Geological Survey operates the National Earthquake Information Center, located in Golden, Colorado. The NEIC issues rapid reports for those earthquakes that register at least 4.5 on the Richter Scale in the United States, or 6.5 on the Richter Scale (or are known to have caused damage) anywhere else in the world. Public warning reports are disseminated in the affected areas via the NWR and EAS systems.

Reference links:

National Communication System: www.disa.mil/info/infov101.html
FEMA National Radio System – Mobile stations: www.fema.gov/r-n-r/mears04.htm
REACT International: www.reactintl.org
Amateur Radio Emergency Service: www.arrl.org/Fand ES/field.pscm/sec1-ch1.html
National Weather Radio: http://205.156.54.206/nwr/index.html
Emergency Alert System (EAS): www.fcc.gov/eb/eas/
Hawaii EAS: http://www.scd.state.hi.us/04_Preparedness/communications/eas/eas.htm
National Earthquake Information Center: http://wwwneic.cr.usgs.gov/ *Enter exactly as shown. There is no dot between "www" and "neic".*
Army MARS: www.asc.army.mil/mars/mars_is_official.htm
SATERN: http://satern.org/satern.html

Review:

Organization is critical to any emergency response. Without an organization that plans and prepares in advance, an Amateur Radio emcomm response is likely to be disorganized and ineffective.

A variety of government and private emergency communication groups assist in time of disaster. While Amateur Radio operators may not interact with many of these systems, it may help to know that they exist, since your served agency may utilize or interact with one or more.

Student activities:

The following activities are designed to familiarize you with the ARES information provided on the ARRL website. Follow the link below and read the ARES information provided:

1. Go to the ARRL website (http://www.arrl.org/). Locate the MOU between ARRL and the American National Red Cross. Answer the following questions:
A. According to the MOU, how is a "disaster" defined?

2. Go to the ARRL web site (http://www.arrl.org/FandES/field/pscm/foreword.html) section entitled "Public Services Communications Manual". Find the answers to the following questions:
A. Is owning emergency-powered equipment a requirement for joining ARES?
B. Who can authorize RACES operation?
C. If the President were to invoke his War Emergency Powers, would there be any restrictions on Amateur Radio operation? If so, how would the two-meter band be affected?
D. What are the two primary components of ARRL's public service field organization? Share the results of both activities with your mentor.

Questions:

1. Which of the following best describes the ARES organizational structure?
A. ARRL –District–Section–County
B. ARRL—Section–District—County
C. ARRL –County–Region–Section
D. ARRL –State – Region–Section

2. Which of the following best describes the ARES chain of command within a Section?
A. Section Manager–District Emergency Coordinator–Emergency Coordinator, Assistant Emergency Coordinator –Section Emergency Coordinator.
B. Section Emergency Coordinator– Section Manager—District Emergency Coordinator–Emergency Coordinator–Assistant Emergency Coordinator.
C. Section Manager–Section Emergency Coordinator–District Emergency Coordinator–Emergency Coordinator–Assistant Emergency Coordinator.
D. Section Manager–Section Emergency Coordinator–Emergency Coordinator District Emergency Coordinator–Assistant Emergency Coordinator.

3. Which of the following best describes a Level 2 RRT?
A. Is a first responder in any emergency.
B. Operates a few strategically placed stations within the first hour of an emergency.
C. Responds within a few hours and is prepared with longer term (72 hour) jump kits.
D. Is always affiliated with SATERN.

4. Which of the following best describes an ARES Mutual Assistance Team (ARESMAT)?
A. Is generally available for tasks lasting less than one day.
B. Is always from the local area.
C. An ARES team who are willing and able to travel to another area.
D. Is called out only when the President suspends regular Amateur operations.

5. *Which of the following is true about REACT?*
A. REACT is a part of ARRL.
B. REACT does not have an MOU with ARRL.
C. REACT's mission is more restricted than that of ARRL.
D. REACT's resources include CB, Amateur Radio, GMRS, FRS, and MURS.

Learning Unit 4

Served Agency Communication Systems

Objective: Emcomm volunteers may be asked to use the agency's own communication systems, in addition to Amateur Radio. This unit attempts to familiarize you with some of the systems you are likely to encounter.

Student preparation required:

Become familiar with the "Continuous Tone Coded Squelch System" (CTCSS), also known by various common trademarks, including Private Line (PL)*, and Channel Guard (CG)*.

    * Private Line is a trademark of Motorola, Inc. - Channel Guard is a trademark of General Electric/Ericcson.

Information:

Going Beyond Amateur Radio

Most served agencies will have their own communication systems and equipment, ranging from modest to complex. In our ever-broadening role as emergency communicators, we may be asked to operate some of this equipment. If this occurs, you must become familiar with its operation.

Your emcomm group should work with the served agency well in advance to determine whether the agency will need you to use its equipment, and under what conditions. Many of these radio systems are quite different from ham radio, and special training may be required.

In addition to different equipment, on-air procedures will definitely be different. Training and drills may be necessary to make Amateur Radio emcomm operators proficient.

State and Local Government Radio Systems:

These systems might include those licensed to police, fire, sheriffs, highway, and other state, county, or city departments. If you are asked to use any of these systems, be sure to learn their standard operating procedures, and "phonetic alphabet" system if one is used. Some departments may use familiar ITU Phonetics, some will use military systems, and still others will make them up as they go along. In addition, a few departments still use a "10 code," but most departments are moving away from special codes in favor of plain language.

Be careful not to lapse into a ham radio operating style. Casual conversations are prohibited by FCC rules and are usually not permitted by the agency. All transmissions must be directly related to the agency's mission.

Many police agencies are licensed for operation on 155.475 MHz, sometimes known as the "National Police Frequency." The FCC has set aside this channel to allow intercommunication between any police agency, regardless of state or jurisdiction. Unfortunately, many departments are not aware of its intended use and treat it as their own private "car to car" channel. Many will not know they have a common channel since they use "channel designators" rather than frequencies. In addition, CTCSS was not supposed to be used on this channel to ensure inter-agency compatibility, but many departments use it anyway. This may become important if different police agencies must intercommunicate with each other in an emergency. If one or more use CTCSS, they will need to disable it by placing their radios in the "monitor" mode, if possible.

Medical Radio Systems:

In order to standardize emergency medical radio systems across the country, the FCC assigned a number of dedicated frequencies. In theory, every ambulance in the country should be equipped to use all these frequencies. In practice, true compatibility is usually limited to a specific region.

The older system, often called "MedStar," used 10 simplex VHF frequencies with a dial-type pulsed-tone encoder to signal specific hospitals. This system is still in use in some rural areas, but is quickly being replaced by more modern systems. The newer Emergency Medical Radio Service uses 10 UHF duplex frequency pairs; one assigned to the hospital, the other to the ambulance, and 7 VHF simplex channels. The UHF channels are known as "Med 1" to "Med 10." In some cases, the hospital's radio is located on a nearby mountain or tall tower in order to achieve the required coverage, and connected to the emergency department by a radio or telephone link.

American Red Cross:

ARC has a nationally licensed frequency (47.42MHz) that can be used by all ARC chapters, primarily for disaster operations. This common channel ensures that ARC units responding from various chapters will be able to communicate with each other. Some chapters also use 47.50MHz. In addition, certain chapters may rent space on commercial systems or license their own VHF or UHF systems for local operations.

Types of Served-Agency Radio Systems

In larger jurisdictions, each agency will probably have its own radio system, completely independent of all other radio users in the same area. This is especially true of large city and state police and fire radio systems. Many agencies have more than one channel, assigned to different purposes. For instance, a fire department might have a "dispatch" channel, and one or more "fireground" channels. This allows local operations at a fire scene to be kept separate from on-going dispatch operations. A police department may have a separate channel for detectives, or one for each precinct. These systems may be on repeaters or use simplex frequencies.

The FCC allocates specific radio frequencies to different types of agencies, and some for multi-agency use. For instance, a frequency designated for use by police agencies may only be used for police business. The same is true of fire radio allocations. "Local Government" allocations may be used for any legitimate local government function.

In addition to "simple" systems where each user group has its own frequency, there are three different types of systems that allow multiple user groups to share resources. These are known as "community repeaters," "trunked repeater systems," and "shared simplex systems."

Community Repeater Systems:

Unlike Amateur Radio repeater systems, a "community" or "shared" repeater uses a different CTCSS tone for each of several user groups. For instance, a city might have one repeater shared by the water, public works, and sanitation departments, licensed as a single "local government" radio system. Since each department uses a different CTCSS tone, they will not normally hear each other's conversations, but only one department can use the system at any given moment. Some very small rural towns may even combine fire and police department operations on the same system, either on a repeater or simplex frequency.

When using any shared frequency -- repeater or simplex -- it is important to press the "monitor" button for a moment before transmitting. This disables the CTCSS decoder, temporarily allowing you to hear any transmissions being made. Some mobile radios automatically switch to "monitor" mode when the mic is removed from its hang-up clip. In this way you can be certain that no one else is using the channel before making your call.

In an emergency situation, these shared channel systems can quickly become overloaded. A common practice is to end all non-essential communications or perhaps move them to an Amateur system instead.

Trunked Systems:

Trunked systems provide an efficient means for several "low volume" users to share a single radio system. They use several co-located repeaters tied together, using computer control to automatically switch a call to an available repeater. When one radio in a group is switched to a new frequency, all the others in the group automatically follow. This is accomplished by having a computer controller move the conversation from frequency to frequency in accordance with a pre-established algorithm. The number of available frequencies in the system depends on its design, and the number of different user groups. Channel switching and assignment data is transmitted on a dedicated channel. Unlike a shared single-frequency repeater system using multiple CTCSS tones, a trunked system will provide almost instant on-demand clear channels in normal usage. Amateur Radio does not currently use this type of system.

In emergency situations, however, most trunked systems suffer from a lack of reserve capacity. To keep designs cost effective, there are usually many more user groups than available channels. The number of available channels is designed to handle the normal day-to-day communications load. When an emergency occurs, these systems can be quickly overloaded with calls, and finding a clear channel can be difficult or impossible.

One "solution" to this problem is to assign certain users or user groups "priority" over others. If all the available channels are occupied, a higher priority user will bump the lowest priority user off the system and take over the channel. Priority status can either be full time or turned on in an emergency depending on the system's design.

Telephone Systems

Telephone systems in use by public service agencies vary greatly. The served agency should be able to provide training in its use. Most telephone systems come with user manuals, and if possible a copy of one should be included in your group's training materials.

Most business telephone systems allow the following basic functions, with which you should be familiar:
- Answering incoming calls
- Placing outside calls
- Placing and answering intercom calls
- Making "speed dial" calls
- Overhead paging
- Placing calls on hold, and then retrieving them.
- Transferring calls to another extension.
- Transferring calls to voice mail, if available
- Retrieving calls from a voice mail box

There may be other, more advanced functions available, but in most cases you will not need to learn them for temporary operations. However, it is always a good idea to keep the user's manual close at hand.

Satellite Systems

Satellite systems in use by public service agencies also vary greatly. Some are used for two-way data and voice communication, others for reception of voice, data, or video. One popular system is the NOAA Emergency Management Weather Information System (EMWINS) system, which allows emergency management officials to obtain up-to-the-second weather maps and information. This system is currently undergoing a complete revision. If your agency is using older equipment, the equipment you learn to use today may soon be replaced.

As with many other served agency systems, the agency will have to provide training in their use if they want you to be able to operate this equipment.

Other Agency-Owned Equipment

In addition to radio and telephone systems, you may need to use fax machines, copiers, computers, and similar devices. Since many of us use these items every day at work, learning their operation should not be a problem in most cases. However, some copiers and computers are quite complicated and may require instruction in their use. Computer software used in public safety applications is usually specially written for the purpose and may require extensive training in the rare situation where you will be required to use the system.

Reference links:

Associated Public Safety Communications Officers (APCO): www.apcointl.org/
FCC – Public Safety Radio Service: http://wireless.fcc.gov/publicsafety/
FCC Rules – Ham Radio: www.arrl.org/FandES/field/regulations/rules-regs.html
International Municipal Signal Association (IMSA): www.imsasafety.org/
Dispatch Magazine: www.911dispatch.com/

Review:

While served agency radio systems may be familiar to Amateur Radio operators, others are not. Both equipment and procedures may vary greatly. If a served agency expects its emcomm volunteers to be able to operate any of its systems, specific training should be provided in advance.

Student activity:

Using the links provided, answer the following questions:
A. What is APCO Project 39? What might Project 39 mean for emcomm operations?
B. What do Sections 97.403 and 97.405 of FCC Rules Part 97 state about Amateur communications during emergencies?
C. Which courses offered by IMSA pertain to radio operations? To what extent do these courses pertain to emcomm operations?
Share the results with your mentor.

Questions:

1. When emcomm team members are called upon to operate on Public Safety Radio Systems, which of the following may they NOT do?
A. Use special "10 codes".
B. Use the served agency's standard operating procedure.
C. Use the phonetic alphabet employed by the served agency.
D. Engage in casual conversations.

2. Which of the following is another trademarked version of Continuous Tone Coded Squelch System (CTCSS)?
A. Private Guard.
B. Private Channel.
C. Line Guard.
D. Private Line.

3. Which of the following best describes the newer Emergency Medical Radio Services?
A. Ten UHF duplex frequencies and seven VHF simplex channels.
B. Ten simplex VHF frequencies with pulsed tone encoders for each hospital.
C. Seven UHF duplex frequencies and ten VHF simplex channels.
D. The MedStar system with channels Med 1 through Med 10.

4. Which one of the following statements is true about trunked systems?
A. Trunked systems are able to operate without the use of computer controllers.
B. The number of frequencies on a trunked system is always a multiple of 10.
C. Amateur radio does not currently use this type of system.
D. Most trunked systems have ample reserve capacity.

5. When emcomm teams work with a served agency, a number of assumptions are made. Which of the following assumptions are true?
A. Amateur radio operators can operate any communication equipment they encounter.
B. There are NO significant differences between amateur radio operating procedures and the procedures used by the served agencies.
C. Served agencies must provide training if amateur operators are to be used effectively.
D. All phonetic alphabets are essentially the same and are thus interchangeable.

Basic Communication Skills

Objective:

This lesson introduces communication skills that are specific to emcomm operations, and helps you understand differences from normal Amateur Radio operations.

Student preparation required:

None

Information:

An emergency communicator must do his part to get every message to its intended recipient, quickly, accurately, and with a minimum of fuss. A number of factors can affect your ability to do this, including your own operating skills, the communication method used, a variety of noise problems, the skills of the receiving party, the cooperation of others, and adequate resources. In this unit, we will discuss basic personal operating skills. Many of the other factors will be covered in later units.

Why Are Emergency Communication Techniques Different?

Life and death communications are not part of our daily experience. Most of what we say and do each day does not have the potential to severely impact the lives and property of hundreds or thousands of people. In an emergency, any given message can have huge and often unintended consequences. An unclear message, one that is delayed or mis-delivered, or never delivered at all can have disastrous results.

Listening

Listening is at least 50% of communication. Discipline yourself to focus on your job and "tune out" distractions. If your attention drifts at the wrong time, you could miss a critical message.

Listening also means avoiding unnecessary transmissions. A wise ham once said, "A ham has two ears and one mouth. Therefore he should listen twice as much as he talks." While you are asking, "when will the cots arrive?" for the fourth time that hour, someone else with a life and death emergency might be prevented from calling for help.

Sometimes the job of listening is complicated by noise. You might be operating from a noisy location, the signal might be weak, or other stations may be causing interference. In each of these cases, it helps to have headphones to minimize local noise and help you concentrate on the radio signal. Digital Signal Processing (DSP) and other technologies may also help to reduce radio noise and interference.

Microphone Techniques

Even something as simple as using your microphone correctly can make a big difference in intelligibility. For optimum performance, hold the mic close to your cheek, and just off to the side of your mouth. Talk across, rather than into, the microphone. This will reduce breath noises and "popping" sounds that can mask your speech.

Speak in a normal, clear, calm voice. Raising your voice or shouting can result in over-modulation and distortion, and will not increase volume at the receiving end. Speak at a normal pace – rushing your words can result in slurred and unintelligible speech. Pronounce words carefully, making sure to enunciate each syllable and sound.

Radios should be adjusted so that a normal voice within 2 inches of the mic element will produce full modulation. If your microphone gain is set so high that you can achieve full modulation with the mic in your lap, it will also pick up extraneous background noise that can mask or garble your voice. A noise-canceling microphone is a good choice since it blocks out nearly all unwanted background noise, and is available in handheld and headset boom mics. Headset boom microphones are becoming less expensive and more popular, but care should be taken to choose one with a cardioid or other noise canceling type element. Many low-cost headset boom mics have omni-directional elements, and will pick up extraneous noise.

"Voice operated transmission" (VOX) is not recommended for emergency communication. It is too easy for background noise and off-air operator comments to be accidentally transmitted, resulting in embarrassment or a disrupted net. Use a hand or foot switch instead.

When using a repeater, be sure to leave a little extra time between pressing the push-to-talk switch and speaking. A variety of delays can occur within a system, including CTCSS decode time, and transmitter rise time. Some repeaters also have a short "kerchunk" timer to prevent brief key-ups and noise from keying the transmitter. It also gives time for some handhelds to come out of the "power-saver" mode. Leaving extra time is also necessary on any system of linked repeaters, to allow time for all the links to begin transmitting. These techniques will ensure that your entire message is transmitted, avoiding time wasting repeats for lost first words.

Lastly, pause a little longer than usual between transmissions any time there is a possibility that other stations may have emergency traffic to pass from time to time. A count of "one, one thousand" is usually sufficient.

Brevity & Clarity

Each communication should consist of only the information necessary to get the message across clearly and accurately. Extraneous information can distract the recipient and lead to misinterpretation and confusion. If you are the message's author and can leave a word out without changing the meaning of a message, leave it out. If the description of an item will not add to the understanding of the subject of the message, leave it out. Avoid using contractions within your messages. Words like "don't" and "isn't" are easily confused. If someone else has drafted the message, work with the author to make it more concise.

Make your transmissions sound crisp and professional, like the police and fire radio dispatchers and the air traffic controllers. Do not editorialize, or engage in chitchat. An emergency net is no place for "Hi Larry, long time no hear," "Hey, you know that rig you were telling me about last month...." or any other non-essential conversation.

Be sure to say exactly what you mean. Use specific words to ensure that your precise meaning is conveyed. Do not say, "that place we were talking about," when "Richards School" is what you mean. Using non-specific language can lead to misunderstandings and confusion.

Communicate *one complete subject* at a time. Mixing different subjects into one message can cause misunderstandings and confusion. If you are sending a list of additional food supplies needed, keep it separate from a message asking for more sandbags. Chances are that the two requests will have to be forwarded to different locations, and if combined one request will be lost.

Plain Language

As hams, we use a great deal of "jargon" (technical slang) and specialized terminology in our daily conversations. Most of us understand each other when we do, and if we do not on occasion it usually makes little difference. In an emergency, however, the results can be much different. A misunderstood message could cost someone's life.

Not everyone involved in an emergency communication situation will understand our slang and technical jargon. Even terms used by hams vary from one region to another, and non-hams will have no knowledge of most of our terminology. Hams assisting from another region might understand certain jargon very differently from local hams.

For these reasons, all messages and communications during an emergency should be in plain language. "Q" signals (except in CW communication), 10 codes, and similar jargon should be avoided. The one exception to this is the list of standard "pro-words" (often called "pro-signs") used in Amateur traffic nets, such as "clear," "say again all after" and so on. We will discuss some of these pro-words in detail below, and others later in this course.

Avoid words or phrases that carry strong emotions. Most emergency situations are emotionally charged already, and you do not need to add to the problem. For instance, instead of saying, "horrific damage and people torn to bits," you might say "significant physical damage and personal injuries."

Phonetics

Certain words in a message may not be immediately understood. This might be the case with an unusual place name, such as "Franconia" or an unusual last name, like "Smythe." The best way to be sure it is understood correctly is to spell it. The trouble is, if you just spell the word using letters, it might still be misunderstood, since many letters sound alike at the other end of a radio circuit. "Z" and "C" are two good examples. For that reason, radio communicators often use "phonetics." These are specific words that begin with the letter being sent. For instance, "ARRL" might be spoken as "alpha romeo romeo lima."

To reduce requests to repeat words, use phonetics anytime a word has an unusual or difficult spelling, or may be easily misunderstood. Do not spell common words unless the receiving station asks you to. In some cases, they may ask for the phonetic spelling of a common word to clear up confusion over what has been received. Standard practice is to first say the word, "I spell," then spell the word phonetically. This lets the receiving station know you are about to spell the word he just heard.

Several different phonetic alphabets are in common use, but most hams and public safety agencies use the ITU Phonetic Alphabet, shown below, and others use military alphabets.

Many hams like to make up their own phonetics, especially as a memory aid for call signs, and often with humorous results. Unfortunately, this practice has no place in emergency communication. In poor conditions, unusual phonetic words might also be misunderstood. We need to be sure that what we say is always interpreted exactly as intended – this is why most professional communicators use standardized phonetics.

ITU Phonetic Alphabet

A - alfa (AL-fa)	B - bravo (BRAH-voh)
C - charlie (CHAR-lee)	D - delta (DELL-tah)
E - echo (ECK-oh)	F - foxtrot (FOKS-trot)
G - golf (GOLF)	H - hotel (HOH-tell)
I - india (IN-dee-ah)	J - juliet (JU-lee-ett)
K - kilo (KEY-loh)	L - lima (LEE-mah)
M - mike (MIKE)	N - november (no-VEM-ber)
O - oscar (OSS-cah)	P - papa (PAH-PAH)
Q - quebec (kay-BECK)	R - romeo (ROW-me-oh)
S - sierra (SEE-air-rah)	T – tango (TANG-go)
U - uniform (YOU-ni-form)	V - victor (VIK-tor)

W - whiskey (WISS-key)	X - x-ray (ECKS-ray)
Y - yankee (YANG-key)	Z - zulu (ZOO-loo)

Numbers are somewhat easier to understand. Most can be made clearer by simply "over-enunciating" them as shown below.

One: "Wun"	Two: "TOOO"
Three: "THUH-ree"	Four: "FOH-wer"
Five: "FY-ive"	Six: "Sicks"
Seven: "SEV-vin"	Eight: "Ate"
Nine: "NINE-er	Zero: "ZEE-row"

Numbers are always pronounced individually. The number "60" is spoken as "six zero," not "sixty." The number "509" is spoken as "five zero nine," and not as "five hundred nine" or "five oh nine."

Pro-words

Pro-words, called "pro-signs" when sent in Morse Code, are procedural terms with specific meanings. They are used to save time and ensure that everyone understands precisely what is being said. Some pro-words are used in general communication, others while sending and receiving formal messages. We will discuss the general words here, and cover the formal message pro-words in a later unit.

Voice	Morse Code*	Meaning and function
Clear	SK	End of contact. In CW, SK is sent before final identification
Over	AR	Used to let a specific station know to respond
Go ahead	K	Used to indicate that any station may respond
Out	CL	Leaving the air, will not be listening
Stand by	AS	A temporary interruption of the contact
Roger	R	Indicates that a transmission has been received correctly and in full

* Two letters are sent as one character   *Source: ARES Field Manual*

Tactical Call Signs

Tactical call signs can identify the station's location or its purpose during an event, regardless of who is operating the station. This is an important concept. The tactical call sign allows you to contact a station without knowing the FCC call sign of the operator. It virtually eliminates confusion at shift changes or at stations with multiple operators.

Tactical call signs should be used for all emergency nets and public service events if there are more than just a few participants.

The NCS may assign the tactical call sign as each location is "opened." Tactical call signs will usually provide some information about the location or its purpose. It is often helpful if the tactical call signs have a meaning that matches the way in which the served agency identifies the location or function. Some examples are:

- "Net" – for net control
- "Springfield EOC" – for the city's Emergency Operations Center
- "Firebase 1" – for the first fire base established, or a primary fire base
- "Checkpoint 1" – for the first check point in a public service event
- "Canyon Shelter" – for the Red Cross shelter at Canyon School
- "Repair 1" – for the roving repair vehicle at a bike-a-thon
- "Mercy" – for Mercy Hospital

Calling with Tactical Call Signs

If you are at "Aid 3" during a directed net and want to contact the net control station, you would say "Net, Aid 3" or, in crisper nets (and where the NCS is paying close attention), simply "Aid 3." If you had emergency traffic, you would say "Aid 3, emergency traffic," or for priority traffic "Aid 3, priority traffic."

Notice how you have quickly conveyed all the information necessary, and have not used any extra words.

If you have traffic for a specific location, such as Firebase 5, you would say "Aid 3, priority traffic for Firebase 5." This tells the NCS everything needed to correctly direct the message. If there is no other traffic holding, the NCS will then call Firebase 5 with, "Firebase 5, call Aid 3 for priority traffic."

Note that no FCC call signs have been used so far. None are necessary when you are calling another station.

Station Identification

In addition to satisfying the FCC's rules, proper station identification is essential to promoting the efficient operation of a net. The FCC requires that you identify at ten-minute intervals during a conversation and at the end of your last transmission. During periods of heavy activity in tactical nets it is easy to forget when you last identified, but if you identify at the end of each transmission, you will waste valuable time. What to do?

The easiest way to be sure you fulfill FCC station identification requirements during a net is to give your FCC call sign as you complete each *exchange*. Most exchanges will be far shorter than ten minutes. This serves two important functions:

1) It tells the NCS that you consider the exchange complete (and saves time and extra words)
2) It fulfills all FCC identification requirements.

Completing a call

After the message has been sent, you would complete the call from Aid 3 by saying "Aid 3, <your call sign>." This fulfills your station identification requirements and tells the NCS that you believe the exchange to be complete.

If the Net Control Station believes the exchange is complete, and Aid 3 had forgotten to identify, then the NCS should say, "Aid 3, do you have further traffic?" At that point, Aid 3 should either continue with the traffic, or "clear" by identifying as above.

A Review of Habits to Avoid
- Thinking aloud on the air: "Ahhh, let me see. Hmm. Well, you know, if…"
- On-air arguments or criticism
- Rambling commentaries
- Shouting into your microphone
- "Cute" phonetics
- Identifying every time you key or un-key the mic
- Using "10" codes, Q-signals on phone, or anything other than "plain language"
- Speaking without planning your message in advance
- Talking just to pass the time.

Reference links:
- For information about **ARRL Public Service Communications**, please see www.arrl.org/FandES/field/pscm/index.html or *The Public Service Communications Manual*.
- For specific information on **ARES**, see the ARRL ARES Field Resources Manual (.pdf file)

Review:

Clear, concise communications save time, and reduce misunderstandings. Avoid any non-essential transmissions. Use tactical call signs to call other stations, and give your FCC call sign only at the end of the complete exchange.

Student activities:

1. Using what you have learned, edit the following exchange to make it clear and concise.

"KA1XYZ at Ramapo Base, this is Bob, K2ABC at Weston EOC calling."

"K2ABC, this is KA1XYZ. Hi, Bob. This is Ramapo Base, Harry at the mic. Go ahead. K2ABC from KA1XYZ."

"KA1XYZ, this is K2ABC returning. Hi, Harry. I have a message for you. By the way, remember to call me later about the get-together the club is having next month. Are you ready to copy the message?" KA1XYZ, this is K2ABC, over to you Harry."

2. Based upon what you have read in this lesson, list five errors to avoid when communicating during an emergency.

Share the results of both activities with your mentor.

Questions:

1. In emergency communication, which one of the following is NOT true?
A. Listening is only about 10% of communication.
B. Any message can have huge and unintended consequences.
C. A message that is never delivered can yield disastrous results.
D. Listening also means avoiding unnecessary communications.

2. Which of the following procedures is best for using a microphone?
A. Hold the microphone just off the tip of your nose.
B. Talk across, rather than into, your microphone.
C. Shout into the microphone to insure that you are heard at the receiving end.
D. Whenever possible, use voice operated transmission (VOX).

3. In emergency communications, which of the following is true?
A. Never use "10 codes".
B. Use "10 codes" when requested on public safety radio systems.
C. Under NO circumstances use "Q" signals on a *CW* net.
D. Use technical jargon when you feel that it is appropriate.

4. Which of the following is always true of a tactical net?
A. Personal call signs are never used.
B. Personal call signs are always preferred over tactical call signs (such as "Aid 3").
C. Personal call signs are required at ten-minute intervals during a conversation **or** at the end of your last transmission.
D. Personal call signs are required at ten-minute intervals during a conversation and at the end of your last transmission.

5. Which of the following is the most efficient way to end an exchange on a tactical net?
A. Say "Over".
B. Say "Roger".
C. Give your FCC call sign.
D. Ask Net Control if there are any further messages for you.

Learning Unit 6

Introduction to Emergency Nets

Objective:

This lesson is intended to provide an overview of operation in a radio network, or "net" environment. It sets the stage for the following lessons, which present various aspects of net operation and message handling in greater detail. We have presented information that is appropriate for local net operations in a variety of settings, and is representative of nets around the country. Local procedures may vary slightly.

Student preparation required:

Learn the following definitions:
- **Net:** A group of stations who gather on one frequency, with a purpose. The net provides a structure and organization to allow an orderly flow of messages.
- **Net Control Station (NCS):** The station in charge of the net and directing the flow of messages and general communications.
- **Formal Messages:** Written messages that are sent in a standardized format.
- **Traffic:** A term referring to messages sent over Amateur Radio, usually formal, written messages.
- **Pass:** to send messages from one station to another.
- **Third Party Traffic:** Messages transmitted on behalf of a person or organization other than a licensed Amateur Radio operator. This term also applies to when a person other than a licensed operator is allowed to use the microphone.
- **Liaison Station:** A station responsible for passing messages between different nets.

Information:

What is an Emergency Net?

The purpose of any net is to provide a means for orderly communication within a group of stations. An "emergency" net is a group of stations who provide communication to one or more served agencies, or to the general public, in an emergency. An emergency net may be formal or informal, depending on the number of participants and volume of messages.

Net Formats

Directed (formal) Nets:
In a directed net, a "net control station" (NCS) organizes and controls all activity. One station wishing to call or send a message to another in the net must first receive permission from the NCS. This is done so those messages with a higher priority will be

handled first, and that all messages will be handled in an orderly fashion. Directed nets are the best format when there are a large number of member stations. (Be careful not to confuse "formal nets" with "formal messages." There is no link between the two.)

Open (informal) Nets:

In an open net, the NCS is optional. Stations may call each other directly. When a NCS is used at all, he usually exerts minimal control over the net. The NCS may step in when the message volume increases for short periods, or to solve problems and keep the net operating smoothly. Open nets are most often used when there are only a few stations and little traffic.

Types of Emergency Nets

Emergency nets may have different purposes, and a given emergency may require one or more of each type of net. During a small operation, all functions may be combined into one net.

- A *traffic net* handles formal written messages in a specified format. The nets operated by the National Traffic System (NTS) are an excellent example of traffic nets. ARES or RACES traffic nets may be directed or open depending on their size.

- *Tactical nets* are used for real-time coordination of activities related to the emergency. This is a faster moving often less formal operation. Messages are usually brief, and frequently unwritten. A tactical net usually has a NCS, but may be directed or open. The NCS may have other duties or responsibilities as well.

- A *resource net* may be needed to acquire volunteers and handle assignments,and is usually a directed net. Resource nets accept check-ins from arriving volunteers, who are then directed to contact an appropriate station or to proceed to a specific location.

- An *information net* is usually an open net used to collect or share information on a developing situation, without overly restricting the use of the frequency by others. Net members send updated local information as needed, and official bulletins from the served agency may be sent by the NCS (if the net has one), an agency liaison station, or an Official Bulletin Station (OBS). The NCS and many of the participants monitor the frequency, but a "roll call" is seldom taken. The operation of an information net also serves as notice to all stations that a more formal net may be activated at any moment if conditions warrant. A good example is a SKYWARN weather net activated during a severe storm watch.

Checking Into an Emergency Net

There are two situations where you will need to "check in" to a net.
- When you first join the net.
- When you have messages, questions, or information to send.

If you are part of the organization operating the net, simply follow the instructions for checking into directed and open nets as discussed below.

To become part of a ***directed net***, listen for the NCS to ask for "check-ins" and listen to any specific instructions, such as "check-ins with emergency traffic only." At the appropriate time, give only your call sign. If you have a message to pass, you can add, "with traffic." If it is an emergency message, say "with emergency traffic." The same is true for stations with priority traffic. Wait for a response before offering more information. Checking into a directed net when the NCS has not asked for check-ins is usually considered a bad practice. However, if a long period passes with no request, you might wait for a pause in the net's activity and briefly call the NCS like this: "Net control, W1FN, with traffic."

To check in to an ***open net*** for the first time, briefly call the net control station as above. If there appears to be no NCS, call anyone on the net to find out who is "in charge" and make contact with them. If you are already part of the net and have a message to send, simply wait for the frequency to be clear before calling another station.

If you are ***not* part of the organization** operating the net, do not just check in and offer to assist. Listen for a while. Be sure you have something specific to offer before checking in, (such as the ability to deliver a message close to your location when none of the regular net members can). If they really do seem to need help that you feel you can provide, you might check in briefly to ask if they have a "resource" net in operation, then switch to that frequency. If not, make a brief offer of assistance to the NCS.

Do not be too surprised if you receive a cool reception to your offer of help. It is usually nothing personal. Emergency nets are serious business. Most emcomm managers prefer to deal with people with known training and capabilities, and with whom they have worked before. You may not have the experience, skills or official credentials they require – and they have no way of knowing what your true capabilities are. Some emcomm managers will assign you as an apprentice, logger, or as a "runner". If you are given such an opportunity, take it! It is all good experience and a great way to introduce you to the group. Better yet, become involved with your local emcomm group now – do not wait for the next disaster.

Passing Messages:

If you told the NCS you have traffic to send when you checked in, he will probably ask you to "list your traffic" with its destination and priority. After you send your list, the NCS will direct you to pass each message to the appropriate station in the net, either on the net frequency, or another frequency to avoid tying up the net. When moving to another frequency to pass the message, always check to see if the frequency is in use before beginning.

When you are asked by the NCS to send your message, the standard procedure is for the NCS to tell the receiving station to call the sending station.

The entire exchange might sound like this:
    NCS: "W1AW, list your traffic."
    You: "W1AW, two priority for Springfield EOC, one welfare for the section net."
    NCS: "Springfield EOC, call W1AW for your traffic."
    Springfield EOC: "W1AW, Springfield EOC, go ahead."
    You: "Number 25, Priority…"
    (After you have sent your messages to the Springfield EOC, the NCS will next direct
    the section net liaison station to call you for their message.)
When you have finished, simply sign with any tactical call sign and your FCC call.

(You will learn more about messages and message handling and "emergency," "priority," and other precedences later in this course.)

"Breaking" the Net

If the net is in progress, and you have emergency traffic to send, you may need to "break" into the net.. Procedures for doing this vary from net to net, but the most common method is to wait for a pause between transmissions and simply say, "Break, WA1ZCN." The NCS will say, "Go ahead WA1ZCN," and you respond, "WA1ZCN with emergency traffic."

Checking Out of an Emergency Net

Always let the NCS know when you are leaving the net, even if it is only for a few minutes. If the NCS believes you are still in the net, they may become concerned about your unexplained absence. This could result in someone being unnecessarily dispatched to check on your well being.

There are three reasons for checking out of (leaving) a net.

- The location of your station is closing.

    If the NCS has given you directions to close the location, simply acknowledge the request, and sign with your tactical call sign, if you are using one, and your FCC call sign. If the order to close has come from a local official, state that your location has been closed, along with the name and title of the official who ordered it, and sign off as above. Long "goodbyes" only tie up the net needlessly,and do not sound very professional.

- You need a break and there is no relief operator.

  Tell the NCS that you will be away from the radio for a certain length of time, the reason, and sign with your tactical call sign, if you are using one, and your FCC call sign.

- You have turned the location over to another operator.

  Tell the NCS that you have turned the station over to (give the new operator's name and FCC callsign), and that you are leaving. Sign with your tactical call sign, if you are using one, and your FCC call sign

There are two special situations to be aware of:

1. If someone asks you in authority, such as a law enforcement officer, to move your station, then move immediately and without argument. Notify the NCS of the situation at the first appropriate opportunity.

2. If someone requests you in authority to turn off your radio, or to refrain from transmitting, do so immediately and *without question*. Do not notify Net Control until you have permission to transmit again, and can do so safely. There is usually a good reason for such a request. It may be an issue of security, or it may be a potential hazard, such as an explosive, which could be triggered by RF energy.

Levels of Nets:

Network systems are often "layered" for greater operating efficiency. Some networks are designed to handle messages within specific areas, and others to handle messages between areas. Think of this much like you would the Interstate Highway System. Local messages (cars) travel between destinations directly on local roads (a local net). When a message has to go to a distant city, it is passed to a regional net (state highway), and if it is *really* distant, to a long distance net (interstate highway). At the other end it is returned to regional, then local nets for delivery. What has been just described is the extensive National Traffic System (NTS), discussed further below.

ARES or RACES can use a similar structure on a smaller scale. For instance, each city might have a local FM net. A county net would handle messages going from city to city. A section HF net would handle messages from county to county. Any net in such a system could have "liaison" stations to pass into the NTS any messages that need to travel out of the section.

The Nets of the National Traffic System

The National Traffic System (NTS) was created by the ARRL and authored by George Hart, W1NJM in 1949 to handle medium and long distance traffic. In an emergency, The National Traffic System can be used to provide a link from the area impacted by the emergency to the outside world. The National Traffic System is a hierarchical (layered) set of nets, beginning at the local level with the Local nets and continuing through the Section Nets, Region Nets, Area Nets, and finally the Transcontinental Corps. Messages are passed by assigned "liaison" stations between various nets as necessary to reach their final destination. These nets operate in carefully designed "cycles" that allow a message to move smoothly and efficiently from one net to the next across the country in 24 hours. Each message follows a pre-determined path to its destination.

The details of NTS operation are quite complex and well beyond the scope of this course. To learn more about the NTS, visit the NTS section of the ARRL website or contact your Section Manager or NTS Section Traffic Manager.

Non-Voice Nets

Emergency Nets may also use other modes of communication besides voice (phone). Traffic nets have used CW since the beginning of Amateur Radio, and it is still a viable option for long distance formal traffic. High speed CW nets can actually handle more messages per hour than most voice nets. Packet communication on VHF and UHF is often used for local communication where accuracy and a record of the message are required. HF digital modes such as AMTOR and PACTOR are used on long distance circuits. Many groups are now experimenting with emergency communication applications for newer modes such as PSK31 on HF and VHF/UHF bands.

Most non-voice nets are directed nets. Packet nets are an exception, due the automatic "store and forward" nature of the mode, and are usually operated as open nets with no NCS.

Reference links:
- To learn about **NTS** in your area, contact your Section Manager (SM), or Section Traffic Manager (STM). To locate your Section Manager (SM), see www.arrl.org/field/org/smlist.html.
- For a **list of ARES and NTS nets** in your area, see *The ARRL Net Directory*
- Recordings of actual emcomm tactical net traffic during the 2000 Alabama tornado:
  http://www.alert-alabama.org/audio.html

Review:

Large nets are usually directed (formal) nets with a NCS in charge. Smaller nets may be "open" (informal), and a NCS is optional. Nets can serve many purposes, including passing formal messages, handling logistics, or passing informal tactical messages. Large emergencies may require that more than one of each type of net – small emergencies may have one combined net. Medium and long distance messages are often handled by the National Traffic System (NTS).

Student activities:

1. Describe the best use of the following nets:
        A. Open nets
        B. Emergency nets
        C. Tactical nets
        D. Resource nets
        E. NTS nets

Share your answers with your mentor.

Questions:

1. Which of the following best describes a net?
A. A group of stations who purposely frequent the airwaves.
B. A group of stations who gather on one frequency with a purpose.
C. A group of stations who occasionally meet on various frequencies.
D. A group of stations who propose to meet at a particular time.

2. What is a major difference between an "open net" and a "directed net"?
A. The presence or absence of full control by a Net Control Station.
B. The presence or absence of formal traffic.
C. The type of radio traffic on the net.
D. The approval or sanction of net operations by the FCC.

3. Which of the following is true of a "tactical net"?
A. The net is used to acquire volunteers and to handle assignments.
B. The net is used for the coordination of activities associated with future emergencies.
C. The net may be directed or open, but will usually have a Net Control Station.
D. The net handles only formal traffic.

4. When should you check in to an emergency net?
A. When you want to comment on something that someone else has said.
B. When you are tired of listening.
C. When you first join the net and when you have messages, questions or relevant information.
D. When you first join the net and when you would like to send greetings to one of the participating stations.

5. *Which of the following is an important rule for emergency nets?*
A. NO FCC call sign is ever used on an emergency net
B. There are NO valid reasons for checking out of a net
C. Because not all Amateur Radio operators are equally proficient with CW, it is NEVER appropriate on an emergency net.
D. If you are requested by someone in authority to refrain from transmitting, do so immediately.

6. *What is the most frequent cause of errors on voice nets?*
A. Speaking too softly.
B. Speaking too rapidly.
C. Failure to write down the message before sending it.
D. Failure to copy the message exactly as it was received.

Basic Message Handling Part I

Objective:

This lesson is intended to provide basic knowledge for both formal and informal message handling, but is not intended to make you an "expert." Further study and practice on your own will be necessary. Level II of this course provides more advanced information on net operations and message handling.

Student Preparation Required:

None

Information:

Consider the following scenario: There are 330 hurricane evacuees in a Red Cross shelter. ARES is providing communications, working in 12-hour shifts. An elderly diabetic woman is brought in at 1400 hours. She will require her next dose of insulin by 2300 hours. The manager goes to the radio room. There is an operator wearing a red baseball hat with funny numbers and letters on it. He asks the operator to inform the county EOC of the medication need. The operator calls the Red Cross EOC and says, "Hey, we have a diabetic lady here who will need insulin by 2300 hours," but doesn't write the message down or log the request.

At 2030 hours the medication has still not been delivered. The shelter manager goes to the radio room to inquire about its status. There is now a different person with a blue baseball cap with a new set of funny letters and numbers. He knows nothing of the earlier request, but promises to "check on it." In the meantime, EOC personnel have discarded the message because it was written on a scrap of paper and had no signature authorizing the order for medication. No one sent a return message requesting authorization.

If each operator had generated and properly logged a formal message, with an authorized signature, it would be a relatively simple matter to track. The informal message has no tracks to follow. Also, by sending a formal message, you are nearly guaranteeing that the receiving station will write it down properly (with a signature) and log it, greatly enhancing it chances of being delivered intact.

Formal vs. Informal Messages

Both formal (written in a specific format) and informal (usually verbal) messages have their place in emergency communication. In general, informal messages are best used for non-critical and simple messages, or messages that require immediate action, those are delivered directly from the author to the recipient. Formal messages are more appropriate when two or more people will handle them before reaching the recipient, or where the contents are critical or contain important details. The most common formal message format is that used by ARRL's NTS, discussed below.

Informal Verbal Messages

Some emergency messages are best sent informally in the interest of saving precious seconds. If you need an ambulance for a severely bleeding victim, you do not have time to compose and send a formal message. The resulting delay could cause the death of the patient.

Other messages do not require a formal written message because they have little value beyond the moment. Letting the net control station know where you are or when you will arrive need not be formal. The message is going directly to its recipient, is simple and clear, and has little detail. Many of the messages handled on a tactical net fit this description.

Formal Written Message Formats

A standard written message format is used so that everyone knows what to expect. This increases the speed and accuracy with which you can handle messages.

The ARRL/NTS message form, or "Radiogram," is a standard format used for passing messages on various nets, and is required for all messages sent through the National Traffic System. While this format may not be perfect for all applications, it serves as a baseline that can be readily adapted for use within a specific served agency. Regular practice with creating and sending messages in any standard format is recommended.

The American Radio Relay League
RADIOGRAM
Via Amateur Radio

Number	Precedence	HX	Station of Origin	Check	Place of Origin	Time Filed	Date
207	P	E	W1FN	10	LEBANON NH	1200 EST	JAN 4

To:

MARK DOE
RED CROSS DISASTER OFFICE
123 MAIN ST
RUTLAND VT 05701

Telephone Number: 802-555-1212

This Radio Message was received at:

Amateur Station_____ Date_____
Name_____
Street Address_____
City, State, Zip_____

NEED   MORE   COTS   AND   SANITATION

KITS   AT   ALL   FIVE   SHELTERS

____   ____   ____   ____   ____

____   ____   ____   ____   ____

____   ____   JOAN SMITH SHELTER MANAGER

	From	Date	Time		To	Date	Time
REC'D				SENT			

A licensed Amateur Radio Operator, whose address is shown above, handled this message free of charge. As such messages are handled solely for the pleasure of operating, a "Ham" Operator can accept no compensation. A return message may be filed with the "Ham" delivering this message to you. Further information on Amateur Radio may be obtained from ARRL Headquarters, 225, Main Street, Newington, CT 06111.

The American Radio Relay League, Inc. is the National Membership Society of licensed radio amateurs and the publisher of QST Magazine. One of its functions is promotion of public service communication among Amateur Operators. To that end, The League has organized the National Traffic System for daily nationwide message handling.

Components of a Standard ARRL/NTS Radiogram:

The standard Radiogram format is familiar to most hams from the pads of yellow-green forms available from ARRL Headquarters. The form has places for the following information:

1. The "Preamble," sometimes referred to as "the header," consists of administrative data such as the message number, originating station, message precedence (importance) and date/time of origination. The combination of the message number and the originating station serves as a unique message identifier, which can be traced if necessary. We will discuss the Preamble in greater detail below.

2. The "Address" includes the name, street address or P.O. box, city, state, and ZIP of the recipient. The address should also include the telephone number with area code since many Radiograms are ultimately delivered with a local phone call.

3. The "Text" of the message should be brief and to the point, limited to 25 words or less when possible. The text should be written in lines of five words (ten if using a keyboard) to make it easier and faster to count them for the "check." Care should be taken to avoid contractions, as the apostrophe is not used in CW. If a word is sent without the apostrophe, its meaning could be lost or changed. The contraction for "I will" (I'll) has a very different meaning when sent without the apostrophe! Contractions are also difficult to understand when sent by phone, especially in poor conditions. Commas and other punctuation are also not used in formal messages. Where needed, the "period" can be sent as an "X" in CW and digital modes, and spoken as "X-RAY." The "X" may be used to seperate phrases or sentences but should be used only when the message would not be clear without it, and never at the end of the text. Question marks can be used as needed, and are usually spoken as "question mark," and sometimes as "query."

4. The "Signature" can be a single name, a name and call sign, a name and a title, "Mom and Dad", and occasionally a return address and phone number – whatever is needed to ensure that the recipient can identify the sender and that a reply message can be sent.

Details of the Preamble:

The preamble or "header" is the section of the ARRL/NTS message form where all the administrative details of the message are recorded. There are eight sections or "blocks" in the preamble. Two of them, "time filed" and "handling instructions," are optional for most messages.

Block #1 - Message Number:

This is any number assigned by the station that first puts the message into NTS format. While any alphanumeric combination is acceptable, a common practice is to use a numeric sequence starting with the number "1" at the beginning of the emergency operation. Stations who are involved in year-round message handling may start numbering at the beginning of each year or each month.

Block #2 Precedence:

The precedence tells everyone the relative urgency of a message. In most cases, a single letter abbreviation is sent with CW or digital modes. On phone, the entire word is always spoken. Within the ARRL/NTS format, there are four levels of precedence:

Routine -- abbreviated with the letter "R." Most Amateur traffic is handled using this precedence it is for all traffic that does not meet the requirements for a higher precedence. In a disaster situation, routine messages are seldom sent.

Welfare -- abbreviated as "W." Used for an inquiry as to the health and welfare of an individual in a disaster area, or a message from a disaster victim to friends or family.

Priority -- abbreviated as "P." For important messages with a time limit; official messages not covered by the EMERGENCY precedence or a notification of death or injury in a disaster area. This precedence is usually associated with official traffic to, from, or related to a disaster area.

EMERGENCY -- there is no abbreviation the word EMERGENCY is always spelled out. Use this for any message having life or death urgency. This includes official messages of welfare agencies requesting critical supplies or assistance during emergencies, or other official instructions to provide aid or relief in a disaster area. The use of this precedence should generally be limited to traffic originated and signed by authorized agency officials. *Due to the lack of privacy on radio, EMERGENCY messages should only be sent via Amateur Radio when regular communication facilities are unavailable.*

Block #3 - Handling Instructions:

This is an optional field used at the discretion of the originating station. The seven standard HX pro-signs are:

HXA -- (Followed by number.) "Collect" telephone delivery authorized by addressee within (X) miles. If no number is sent, authorization is unlimited.

HXB -- (Followed by number.) Cancel message if not delivered within (X) hours of filing time; service (notify) originating station.

HXC -- Report date and "time of delivery" (TOD) to originating station.

HXD – Report to originating station the identity of the station who delivered the message, plus date, time and method of delivery. Also, each station to report identity of station to which relayed, plus date and time.

HXE -- Delivering station to get and send reply from addressee.

HXF -- (Followed by date in numbers.) Hold delivery until (specify date).

HXG -- Delivery by mail or telephone - toll call not required. If toll or other expense involved, cancel message, and send service message to originating station.

If more than one HX pro-sign is used, they can be combined like this: HXAC. However, if numbers are used the HX must be repeated each time. On voice, use phonetics for the letter or letters following the HX to ensure accuracy, as in "HX Alpha."

Block #4 - Station of Origin:

This is the FCC call sign of the first ham that put the message into NTS format. It is not the message's original author. For instance, you are the radio operator for a Red Cross shelter. The fire station down the street sends a runner with a message to be passed and you format and send the message. You are the "Station of Origin," and fire station is the "Place of Origin," which will be listed in Block 6.

Block #5 The Check:

The check is the number of words in the text section only. Include any "periods" (written as "X," spoken as "X-Ray"). The preamble, address and signature are not included. After receiving a message, traffic handlers count the words in the message and compare the word count to the Check in the preamble. If the two numbers do not agree, the message should be re-read by the sending station to verify that all words were copied correctly. If the message was copied correctly and an error in the check exists, do not replace the old count with the new count. Instead, update the count by adding a "slash" followed by the new count. For example, if the old count was five, and the correct count was six, change the check to "5/6". For more information on counting words and numbers for the check, follow this link.

Block #6 - Place of Origin:

This is the community or building where the originator of the message is located, whether ham or not. This is not the location of the ham that first handled the message, which is listed in Block 4, "Station of Origin."

Block #7 - Time Filed:

This is an optional field unless "Handling Instruction Bravo" (HXB) is used. HXB means "cancel if not delivered within X hours of filing time." Unless the message is time sensitive, this field may be left blank for routine messages, but completing the time field is generally recommended. During emergencies, use "local time" with indicators such as PST or EDT to eliminate confusion by emergency management personnel.

Block #8 Date:

This is the date the message was first placed into the traffic system. Be sure to use the same date as the time zone indicated in Block 7.

Header Examples:

This is how a complete header might look for a CW or digital message:
    NR207 R HXA50 W4MLE 10 SPRINGFIELD OH 1200EST JAN 4

This is how the same header would be spoken:
    "Number two zero seven Routine HX Alpha five zero Whiskey Zero Mike Lima
    Echo One Two   Springfield Ohio   One Two Zero Zero local   January four." A
    brief pause is made between each block to help the receiving station separate the
    information.

Pro-Words and Pro-Signs:

When sending formal traffic, standard "pro-words" or pro-signs" (CW) are used to begin or end parts of the message, and to ask for portions of the message to be repeated. In addition to adding clarity, the use of standard pro-words and pro-signs save considerable time.

Some pro-words and pro-signs tell the receiving station what to expect next in the address, text, and signature portions of the message – they are *not* used while reading the header, since the header follows a pre-determined format. Examples of commonly used pro-words are, "figures" sent before a group consisting of all numerals, "initial" to indicate that a single letter will follow, or "break" to signal the transition between the address and the text, and the text and the signature.

MESSAGE HANDLING PRO-WORDS, PROSIGNS AND ABBREVIATIONS

Pro-Word	Pro-Sign (CW)	Meaning or Example
BREAK	BT *	Separates address from text and text from signature.
CORRECTION	HH *	"I am going to correct an error."
END	AR *	End of message.
MORE	B	Additional messages to follow.

NO MORE	N	No additional messages. In CW can also mean "negative" or "no"
FIGURES	Not needed	Used before a word group consisting of all numerals.
INITIAL	Not needed	Used to indicate a single letter will follow.
I SAY AGAIN	IMI *	Used to indicate a repeat of a word or phrase will follow.
I SPELL	Not needed	"I am going to spell a word phonetically."
LETTER GROUP	Not needed	Several letters together in a group will follow. Example: ARES, SCTN.
MIXED GROUP	Not needed	Letters and numbers combined in a group will follow. Example: 12BA6
X-RAY	X	Used to indicate end of sentence, as with a "period."
BREAK	BK *	Break; break-in; interrupt current transmission on CW
CORRECT	C	Correct, yes
CONFIRM	CFM	Confirm (please check me on this)
THIS IS	DE	Used preceeding indentification of your station
HX	HX	Handling instructions, single letter to follow – optional part of preamble
GO AHEAD	K	Invitation for specific station to transmit
ROGER	R	Message understood. In CW, may be used for decimal point in context
When receiving formal traffic, the following pro-words, always preceded by "Say Again", are used to ask for clarification or repeats of missing words.		
WORD AFTER	WA	``Say again word after..."
WORD BEFORE	WB	``Say again word before..."
BETWEEN	-	``Say again between...and ...."
ALL AFTER	AA *	``Say again all after..."
ALL BEFORE	AB	``Say again all before..."
*** Two letters are sent as one character.** Additional CW abbreviations are covered in a later Learning Unit.*		

Sending a Message with Voice:

When the receiving station is ready to copy, read the message at a pace that will allow the receiving station to write it down. If the receiving station has missed any portion of the message, they will say, "say again all after____," or "say again all between____ and ____." In some nets, the practice is to say "break" and then unkey between sections of the message so that a station can ask for missing words to be repeated (these repeated words are also known as "fills"). In many nets the entire message is read first before any fills are requested. All numbers are spoken individually, as in "three two one five," not "thirty-two fifteen," or "three thousand two hundred and five."

Here is the entire message as it would be spoken:

"Number two zero seven   Routine   HX Alpha five zero Whiskey Zero Mike Lima Echo One Zero   Springfield Ohio   one two zero zero local   January four.
Mark Doe
Red Cross Disaster Office
Figures one two three Main Street
Columbus Ohio figures one two three four five
Figures three two one five five five one two one two
Break
Need more cots and sanitation kits at all five shelters
Break
Max Percy Shelter Manager
End   No more"

Time Savers

What NOT to say:

When passing formal traffic, do not add unnecessary words. Since the parts of the header are always sent in the same order, there is no need to identify them. Here is an example of how *not* to read the header and address of a message on the air:

> Number two zero seven Routine HX Alpha five zero   station of origin W0MLE check 10   time one two zero zero   Springfield Ohio   January 4
> Going to Mark Doe   Red Cross Disaster Office
> Address figures one two three Main Street Columbus Ohio
> ZIP figures one two three four five
> Telephone Figures three two one five five five one two one two

This example added nine unneeded words to the message, including "station of origin," "check," "time," "going to," "address," "ZIP," and "telephone." If there is something about the message that deviates from the standard format, or if an inexperienced operator is copying the message without a pre-printed form, then some additional description may be necessary, but in most cases it just wastes time. (The pro-word "figures" is used correctly, and "number" is always spoken before the message number.)

Reference links:

- For a **list of ARES and NTS nets** in your area, see The ARRL Net Directory
- For a detailed discussion of the **FCC Rules on emergency and third party communications**, please see the ARRL *FCC Rule Book*, Chapter 5.
- Precedences and handling instructions – ARRL web site
- NTS and ARES forms – NTS message blanks, instructions, etc - ARRL web site
- FSD218 Message Form Card (also known as the "Pink Card")

Review:

Formal messages are more likely to be delivered intact than verbal comments. Using a standard format for formal messages makes it easier and faster for both sending and receiving stations to handle.

Student activity:

Compose three complete ARRL/NTS formatted messages, one for each Precedence. Use Handling Instructions and include the time and date sent. To determine the word count for the check, refer to this link. Share them with your mentor.

Questions:

1. The preamble to an ARRL Radiogram message contains a block called "Precedence." Which of the following represents the correct precedence for an EMERGENCY message?
A. "URGENT".
B. "U".
C. "EMERGENCY".
D. "E".

2. The preamble to an ARRL Radiogram message contains a block called "Handling Instructions." What is the meaning of the handling instruction "HXE"?
A. Delivering station to get and send reply from addressee.
B. Report date and time of delivery to originating station.
C. Cancel message if not delivered within (X) hours of filing time.
D. Collect telephone delivery authorized.

3. ARRL Radiogram messages contains a block called "Time Filed." Which of the following is true of entries in that block?
A. This field is always completed.
B. Time entries are always Universal time.
C. During emergencies "local time" is used.
D. During emergencies "local time" along with the local date is used.

4. ARRL Radiogram messages contains a block called "The Check." Which of the following is true of entries in that block?
A. The check contains a count of the words in the entire message.
B. The check contains a count of the words in the preamble and the text of the message.
C. The check contain a count of the words in the preamble, address and text of the message.
D. The check contains a count of the words in the text of the message.

5. *Which of the following statements is true of punctuation within an ARRL Radiogram?*

A. Punctuation is always helpful; it should be used whenever possible.

B. Punctuation is rarely helpful; it should never be used.

C. Punctuation should be used only when it is essential to the meaning of the message.

D. The comma and apostrophe are the most common punctuation signs used in NTS messages.

Basic Message Handling Part II

Objective:

This unit is a continuation of the previous Learning Unit.

Student preparation required:

No additional preparation is required.

Information:

Message Handling Rules

Do not speculate on anything relating to an emergency! There may be hundreds of people listening to what you say (other Amateurs, and the media and general public using scanners) and any incorrect information could cause serious problems for the served agency or others. You do not want to be the source of any rumor.

If your served agency requests an estimate, you can provide that information as long as you make it very clear that it is only an estimate as you send it. For example, saying, "The estimated number of homes damaged is twelve" would be acceptable.

Pass messages exactly as written:

In addition to speed, your job as a communicator is to deliver each message as accurately as possible. Therefore, you must not change any message as you handle it. If it is longer than you would like, you must send it anyway. Apparently misspelled words or confusing text must be sent exactly as received. Only the original author may make changes. If you note an inaccurate word count in a NTS format message, you must maintain the original count and follow it with the actual count received at your station, i.e.: "12/11."

Should you return a message to the author before first sending it if it seems incorrect or confusing? This is a judgment call. If the apparent error will affect the meaning of the message and the author is easily contacted, it is probably a good idea. Whenever possible, it is a good practice to read messages carefully in the presence of the author before accepting them. This way, potential errors or misunderstandings can be corrected before the message is sent.

Non-Standard Format Messages:

Much of the tactical information being passed during a major emergency will not be in NTS format. It may have much of the same information, but will be in a non-standard format. These messages should also be passed exactly as received.

The Importance of the Signature

During an emergency, the messages you handle can easily contain requests for expensive supplies that have a very limited "shelf life" (such as blood for an aid station), or for agencies that will only respond to authorized requests (i.e.: for medevac helicopters). For this reason, it is critical that you include that the signature and title of the sender in every message.

ARRL Numbered Radiograms

ARRL Numbered Radiograms are a standardized list of often-used phrases. Each phrase on the list is assigned a number. There are two groups: Group One is for emergency relief and consists of 26 phrases numbered consecutively from "ONE" to "TWENTY SIX," and preceded by the letters "ARL." For example, "ARL SIX" means "will contact you as soon as possible."

Group Two contains 21 routine messages, including number "FORTY SIX" and from "FIFTY" through "SIXTY NINE." Earlier printed versions of this list do not contain the latest additions. For the complete list, see
http://www.arrl.org/FandES/field/forms/fsd3.pdf

When using numbered radiograms, the letters "ARL" are placed in the "check" block of the preamble, just prior to the number indicating the word count, as in "ARL7."

In the text of the message, the numbered radiogram is inserted by using the letters "ARL" as one word, followed by the number written out in text, not numerals. For example: "ARL FIFTY SIX."

It is important to spell out the numbers letter by letter when sending using voice. This allows the receiving station to correctly copy what is being sent, and not inadvertently write the figures out as "FIVE SIX" instead of "FIFTY SIX."

"ARL FIFTY SIX" is counted as three words for the "check" block. Two common receiving errors are to write "ARL-56" and count it as one word, or "ARL 56" and count it as two words.

Some numbered messages require a "fill in the blank" word in order to make sense. Here are two examples:
ARL SIXTY TWO: Greetings and best wishes to you for a pleasant _____ holiday season.
ARL SIXTY FOUR: Arrived safely at _____.

Here's an example of a message to convey a Christmas greeting, indicate safe arrival and send regards from family members.

57 R W1AW ARL 16 PUEBLO CO   DECEMBER 10
RICHARD RYAN
3820 S SUNNYRIDGE LANE
NEW BERLIN WISCONSIN 53151
414 555 1234
BREAK
ARL FIFTY ARL SIXTY TWO CHRISTMAS ARL SIXTY FOUR HOME
MOM AND DAD SEND THEIR LOVE
BREAK
BOB AND ALICE

Note that no "XRAY" is used between parts of this message. The numbered radiogram assumes a period at the end of the phrase.

Important: Be sure to decode a message containing an ARL text into plain language before delivering it. Chances are good that the recipient will not know the meaning of the ARL code number.

Copying Hints

When copying the text of a message by hand, receiving stations should write five words on each line, (or ten words per line if using a keyboard). The yellow and green ARRL Radiogram form is set up for hand copying with spaces for each word, but even if you are writing on whatever happens to be handy, grouping the words five to a line allows for a very quick count after the message is received. Once complete, the receiving operator compares the word count with the check. If okay, the message is "rogered" – if not, the message is repeated at a faster reading speed to locate the missing or extra words.

Modified Message Form for Disasters

While ARRL/NTS format messages can handle many different types of information flow, there can be requirements for formats that are unique to an individual agency or type of emergency. Your emcomm group should work with each served agency *before* the emergency to see which format will best fulfill their needs.

Service Messages

A "service message" is one that lets the originating station know the status of a message they have sent. A service message may be requested by a handling instruction (HX), or may be sent by any operator who has a problem delivering an important message. During emergencies, service messages should only be sent for Priority and Emergency messages.

Logging and Record Keeping

An accurate record of formal messages handled and various aspects of your station's operation can be very useful. Lost or misdirected messages can be tracked down later on, and a critique of the operation afterward can be more accurate. All logs should include enough detail to be meaningful later on, especially the date and an accurate time. With some agencies, your log becomes a legal document and may be needed at some later time should an investigation occur. In this case, logs should be completed and turned in to the appropriate person for safekeeping and review.

What to Log:

Log all incoming and outgoing messages. Record the name of the sender, addressee, the station that passed the message to you, the station to whom the message was sent, the message number, and the times in and out. Keep the written copy of each message in numerical order for future reference.

Also, log which operators are on duty for any given period, and record any significant events at your station. These might include changes in conditions, power failures, meals, new arrivals and departures, equipment failures, and so on.

In addition to the log, copies of all messages should be kept and catalogued for easy retrieval if needed later for clarification or message tracking. Many operators make notes about when the message was received and sent, and to and from whom, directly on the message form itself. This helps speed up tracking later on. Never rely on your memory.

Should informal messages be logged? This is usually up to the stations involved, and depends on the circumstances. Even informal messages can contain important details that may be need to be recalled later. Emergency or Priority messages of any kind should always be logged. Many net control operators like to log every message or exchange, no matter how inconsequential. Others like to log only those with potentially important details.

Log Formats:

At a station with little traffic, all information can be included in one chronological log. However, if a large number of messages are being handled and you have a second person to handle logging, separate logs can make it faster and easier to locate information if it is needed later. You might keep one log for incoming messages, one for outgoing messages, and a third for station activities. The NCS will also need to keep a log of which operators are assigned to each station and the times they go one and off duty.

Who should log?

At the net level, logging can be handled in several ways. If activity is low, the net control operator can handle logging. In busy nets, a second person can keep the log as the net's "secretary" and act as a "second set of ears" for the NCS. The logger can be at the NCS, or they might be listening from a different location.

If an "alternate NCS" station has been appointed, they should keep a duplicate log. If they need to "take over" the net at any point, all the information will be at hand, preserving the continuity of the net.

In addition to logs kept at the net level, each individual operator should keep his or her own log. This will allow faster message tracking and provides duplicate information should one station's logs be lost or damaged.

In a fast moving tactical net, keeping a log while on the move may be impossible. In this case, the net control station may decide to keep one log detailing the various informal messages passed on the network.

Logging is a good position for a trainee with limited experience, or an unlicensed volunteer. Two experienced and licensed operators can also alternate between on-air and logging duties to help combat fatigue.

Writing Techniques for Message Copying and Logging

Your logs should be clear and legible to be of any use. If only you can read your handwriting, the log will be of little value to the operator who takes the next shift. Print in neat block letters on lined paper or a pre-printed log form. A firm writing surface with support for your forearm will reduce fatigue and improve legibility.

Keep both pens and pencils on hand since each works better under different conditions. Some operators prefer special "diver's" pens that will write on wet surfaces at any angle.

Logs should be kept in spiral bound notebooks to prevent pages from becoming lost. In the case of pre-printed log sheets, a three-ring binder works well. If more than one log is kept, each should be in its own notebook to prevent confusion and accidental entries.

In fast-moving situations, it can be difficult or impossible to keep a log of any kind. If a message, exchange, or event should be logged, try to do it as soon as possible afterwards, or ask the NCS to add it as a notation in his log.

Message Authoring – Them or us?

One of the oldest arguments in emcomm is the question of whether or not emcomm personnel should author (create) agency-related official messages. If your job is strictly communication, and the message is not about the communication function you are providing, the best answer is "no." "Pure" communicators are not generally in a position to create messages on behalf of the served agency. They have no direct authority and usually lack necessary knowledge.

However, you should always work with a message's author to create text that is short, to the point, and uses the minimum number of words necessary. Once you do this with most agency personnel, they will be happy to send you appropriate messages, since it saves them time, too. If the author tells you to "just take care of the wording for me," it is still a good idea to get their final approval and signature before sending the message.

If you have additional training for an agency-specific job that involves message origination, this is quite different from the situation of a "pure" communicator. In this case, you *do* have the training and authority necessary to generate an official message.

Other messages that can and should be generated by all emcomm operators are those that deal solely with communication. Examples would be messages about net operations and frequencies, and requests for relief operators, radio equipment, supplies, food, and water for emcomm personnel.

Message Security & Privacy

Information transmitted over Amateur Radio can never be totally secure, since FCC rules strictly prohibit us from using any code designed to obscure a message's actual meaning. Anyone listening in with a scanner can hear all that is said on voice nets. The federal Communications Privacy Act does not protect amateur Radio communications, and anything overheard may be legally revealed or discussed. Reporters in disaster-prone areas have been known to purchase digital-mode-decoding software for laptops in order to intercept ham radio communications during disasters.

However, this does not mean that you can discuss any message you send with others. Messages sent via Amateur Radio should be treated as privileged information, and revealed only to those directly involved with sending, handling, or receiving the message. This must be done to offer at least a minimum level of message security. You cannot prevent anyone from listening on a scanner, but you can be sure they do not get the information directly from you.

Your served agency should be made of aware of this issue, and must decide which types of messages can be sent via Amateur Radio, and using which modes. The American Red Cross has strict rules already in place. In general, any message with personally identifiable information about clients of the served agency should be avoided – this is a good policy to follow with any agency if you are in doubt. Messages relating to the death of any specific person should never be sent via Amateur Radio. Sensitive messages should be sent using telephone, landline fax, or courier.

While we can never guarantee a message will not be overheard, there are ways to reduce the likelihood of casual listeners picking up your transmissions. Here are some ideas:
- Use a digital mode: packet, PSK31, fax, RTTY, AMTOR, etc.
- Pick an uncommon frequency – stay off regular packet nodes or simplex channels.
- Do not discuss frequencies or modes to be used on voice channels.
- Avoid publishing certain ARES or RACES net frequencies on web sites or in any public document.

Some agencies use a system of "fill in the blank" data gathering forms with numbered lines. To save time on the radio, all that is sent is the line number and its contents. A casual listener might hear, "Line 1, 23; line 5, 20%; line 7, zero." The receiving station is just filling in the numbered lines on an identical form. Without the form, a casual listener will not have any real information. As long as encryption is not the primary intent, this practice should not violate FCC rules.

Refernce links

<u>ARRL F&ES – Appendix A – Originating Messages</u>

Review:

In this unit you learned how to format, send, and receive a formal NTS style message, and the importance of the signature, logging, and accuracy. Formal message formats make message handling more efficient and accurate. Not every situation requires a formal message, but where the accuracy of specific information is critical, the formal message is the best method.

Amateur Radio is not a secure mode, but you can take other steps to protect messages. You should never discuss the contents of messages with anyone else.

Officials of a served agency normally originate messages, but if you have additional training in a job for your served agency, you may also be authorized to originate messages. Whenever possible, you should work with a message's author to create a clear text using the minimum number of words necessary.

Student activities:

1. Create a formal NTS style message using an ARL numbered radiogram text. Be sure the word count is correct.

2. Edit the following message text to reduce the number of words to a minimum, without losing any clarity.
"We need 50 additional cots and blankets at the Roe School shelter, and we also need more food since 20 new people just arrived and we are told another 30 may be coming soon. Please call me and tell me when these supplies will arrive."

3. Go to the ARRL website and look up ARRL Numbered Radiograms:
http://www.arrl.org/FandS/field/forms/fsd3.pdf
When you have located the list of Numbered Radiograms, answer the questions that follow. Which of the Radiograms:
    A. Indicates that a medical emergency exists?
    B. Requests additional radio operators?
    C. Offers congratulations on a new baby?

D. Offers greetings for a merry Christmas and happy New Year
E. Indicates safe arrival.

Share these your with your mentor.

Questions:

1. As part of an EMCOMM group handling message traffic in an emergency, you are asked to forward a message that contains typographical errors. Which of the following is your best course of action?
A. Delay sending the message.
B. Forward the message exactly as received.
C. Return the message to the originating station.
D. On your own, correct the error in the message and forward it.

2. As part of an EMCOMM net handling message traffic in an emergency, you are asked to forward a message in a non-standard format. Which of the following is your best course of action?
A. Delay sending the message until you have conferred with the originator.
B. Return the message to the originator.
C. On your own, rewrite the message in proper format and forward it.
D. Forward the message exactly as received.

3. You have been asked to send an ARRL Radiogram dealing with birthday greetings. Which of the following is the correct format for the message?
A. "ARRL 46"
B. "ARL 46"
C. "ARL FORTY SIX"
D. "ARRL FORTY SIX"

4. When delivering an ARRL numbered radiogram, which should be done?
A. Deliver the message exactly as received.
B. Deliver the message exactly as received but add your own written explanation.
C. Decode the message into plain language before delivery.
D. Deliver the message exactly as received but add your own verbal explanation.

*5. During an emergency, **service messages** should only be sent for which of the following categories of message?*
A. Emergency, Priority, Welfare and Routine
B. Emergency, Priority and Welfare
C. Priority and Welfare
D. Emergency and Priority

Learning Unit 9

Net Operating Guidelines

Objective:

This unit will help you understand how to operate efficiently and effectively in a net environment under emergency conditions.

Student preparation required:

None

Information:

In previous lessons you learned about the various types of nets, and how they function in a general sense. In this lesson, we will talk about the job of the Net Control Station (NCS) and other net officials, and some common issues encountered in net operations.

The Net Manager

Every organization needs an executive level manager to oversee the entire operation and ensure that everything runs smoothly. Depending on the type of net, the Net Manager will be responible for recruiting and training NCS operators, liaison stations, and other net members. The Net Manager sets up the net's schedule and makes sure that one or more qualified NCS operators will be available for each session of the net. In a long-term emergency net, the Net Manager may also arrange for relief operators and support services.

The NCS

Think of the NCS as a "ringmaster" or "traffic cop." The NCS decides what happens in the net, and when. If the EOC has a Priority message for Red Cross Shelter 1, and Medical Station 4 has an Emergency message for Mercy Hospital, it is the NCS's job to make sure that the Emergency message is sent first. He decides when stations will check in, with or without traffic, and whether messages will be passed on the net frequency or a different one. The NCS needs to be aware of everything going on around him and handle the needs of the net, its members, and served agency as quickly and efficiently as possible. It can be a daunting task in a busy and challenging net.

The NCS can be located anywhere, but should be in a position to hear most, if not all, stations in the net. This helps avoid time consuming "relays." Some groups place their NCS at the EOC or command post, others like to keep them away from the noise and confusion.

The NCS is in charge of a specific net, but should not be responsible for the entire emcomm operation. That is the job of the EC or similar emcomm manager. It is not possible to be in command of all aspects of an emergency response, and still run a net effectively, since both jobs require 100% of your attention.

Net Scripts

Many groups open and close their nets with a standard script. The text of the script lets listeners know the purpose and format of the net. Using a standard script also ensures that the net will be run in a similar format each time it operates, regardless of who is acting as the NCS. A typical net script might look like this:

> **Opening:** *This is [call sign], net control station for the New Hampshire ARES/RACES Emergency Net. This is a directed emergency net for liaison stations from all New Hampshire ARES/RACES regions. Please transmit only when requested to, unless you have emergency traffic.*
>
> *Any stations with emergency traffic, please call now. (Stations call in and emergency traffic is passed.)*
>
> *Any stations with priority traffic, please call now. (Stations call in and priority traffic is passed.)*
>
> *All other stations with or without traffic, please call now. (Stations call in and any traffic is passed.)*
>
> **Closing:** *I would like to thank all stations that checked in. This is [call sign] securing the New Hampshire ARES/RACES Emergency Net at [date and time] returning the [repeater or frequency] to regular use.*

The Backup NCS

A backup NCS needs to be readily available should there be an equipment failure at the primary NCS location, or if the primary NCS operator needs to take a break There are two types of backup NCS. Either the Net Manager or the primary NCS, depending on the situation appoints both. All members of the net should be made aware of the backup NCS assignment early in the net's operation.

The first type is at the same location as the primary NCS operator. The second is a station at a different location that maintains a duplicate log of everything happening during the net. Whenever possible, an offsite backup NCS should be maintained, even if an on-site backup is present. This is especially important during an emergency where antennas can be damaged or power lost. Equipment can fail even during less demanding operations.

Acting as a "fill-in" NCS

Even before you have had a chance to be trained by your group to act as a NCS operator, an opportunity might arise for you handle the job temporarily. During an emergency, anyone and everyone can be asked to take on new and unfamiliar tasks in order to deal with a rapidly changing situation. Fortunately, basic NCS skills are not difficult to teach or learn. Here are some basic dos and don'ts:

- Remember that although you are in control of the net, you are not "God." Treat members with respect and accept suggestions from other experienced members.
- If you are taking over an existing net, try to run it much as the previous NCS did.
- Always follow a script if one is provided. Write your own if necessary.
- Handle messages in order of precedence: Emergency – Priority – Welfare.
- Speak clearly and in a normal tone of voice. Use good mic technique.
- Make all instructions clear and concise, using as few words as possible.
- Keep notes as you go along. Do not let your log fall behind.
- Write down which operators are at which locations. When one leaves or is replaced, update your notes.
- Ask stations to pass messages off the main net frequency whenever possible.

All the reading and study in the world will not replace actual experience. You should look for opportunities to practice being the NCS operator well before an emergency occurs.

Net Members

Operators at various sites are responsible for messages going to and from their location. They must listen to everything that happens on the net, and maintain contact with the served agency's people at the site. They assist the served agency with the creation of messages, put them into the appropriate format, and contact the NCS when they are ready to be sent.

Whenever possible, two operators should be at each site. When the net is busy, one can handle logging, message origination, and work with the served agency's staff while the other monitors the net and copies incoming traffic. During slower periods, one member can be "off-duty" for rest, meals, or personal needs.

Bulletin Stations

In some nets, the NCS does not send out bulletins and other incident related information. That is the role of the "bulletin station." This station relays bulletins authorized by the served agency to all stations in the net. They may also be transmitted on a preset schedule, such as at the top and bottom of each hour. The bulletin station must be located at the served agency or have a reliable communication link to them.

Liaison Stations

Liaison stations pass messages between two different nets. These stations are usually "appointed" by the NCS or Net Manager, depending on the type of organization. Messages may be passed as needed, or on a pre-set schedule. In some cases, a liaison station will monitor one net full time. When a message must be passed to another net, they leave the net temporarily to pass it, and then return. The other net has a liaison station who does exactly the same thing, but in reverse.

In other situations, a single liaison station may need to handle messages going both ways between two nets. There are two ways to do this. You can use two radios to monitor both nets at the same time, a difficult task if either or both nets are busy. The radio antennas must be separated sufficiently to prevent interference between radios when one is used to transmit. In the second method, one radio is used, and the liaison station switches between the two nets on a rotating schedule.

Relay Stations

While not a regular net position, a relay station is one that passes messages between two stations in the net that cannot hear each other. Relay stations are generally designated by the NCS on an "as needed" basis.

Workload and Shift Changes

Although it happens frequently, no operator should try to work excessively long hours. When you become tired, your efficiency and effectiveness decline, and your served agency is not getting the best possible service. Net managers and NCS operators should work with the EC or other emcomm manager to ensure that all net members get some rest on a regular basis.

It is a good practice for any replacement NCS, liaison, or net member to monitor the net for at least fifteen minutes and review the logs with the present operator before taking over. This assures continuity in the net's operation.

Non-voice Modes

Packet modes include FM packet, HF packet, and PACTOR. Because packet modes can provide an automatic connection between two stations, it is not really proper to speak of a "packet net." Although messages can be transmitted between two stations "keyboard to keyboard" as with RTTY or PSK31, it is usually better to transmit them as "traffic," using the bulletin board or mailbox facility of the terminal node controller (TNC). Packet messages are automatically routed and stored without any action by the receiving station's operator or a NCS.

Non-packet digital modes are not automatic, and may require a NCS operator to manage the net in much the same way as a phone or CW net. These include RTTY, PSK31, AMTOR, and GTOR.

CW Procedures: A good "fist" at 10 words per minute is better than a sloppy "fist" at 30 words per minute. Sending speed is not a true measure of effectiveness, but accuracy is. When propagation or interference makes communication difficult, or when the receiving operator cannot keep up, it is time to reduce the sending speed. Always send at a speed that the receiving station can copy comfortably.

There are variations used when passing traffic via CW, especially when both stations are operating "full break-in" mode (both stations are capable of receiving signals between each Morse character sent). The receiving station can "break" (stop) the sending station at any point for needed fills, instead of waiting for the entire message to be sent. There are additional special pro-signs used, and interested Amateurs should be familiar with ARRL publication FSD-218. This publication is sometimes referred to as the "pink card" and contains CW net procedures as well as a description of the Amateur Message Form, message precedence, and Handling Instruction abbreviations.

Procedure Signals (Prosigns) for Morse Code

BK	Invite receiving station to transmit (break)
CL	Going off the air (clear)
CQ	Calling any station (literally, Come Quick)
K	Go, invite any station to transmit
R	All received OK
AA	(Separation between parts of address or signature)
AR	Over, end of message
AS	Please stand by
BT	Separation (break) between address and text; between text and signature
KN 'X'	Go only, invite a specific station 'X' to transmit
SK	End of contact (send before sending your call)

Abbreviations

Fill	Term used to describe missing items (words, characters, numbers etc.) when handling messages in the National Traffic System.
AA	All after (use to get fills)
AB	All before (use to get fills)
ADEE	Addressee (name of the person to whom the message is addressed)
ARL	(Used with "check" - indicates use of ARL numbered message in text.)
BN	Between
SIG	Signed; signature (last part of message)
WA	Word after
WB	Word before

When formatting an ARRL Radiogram message, use abbreviations and prosigns consistently and appropriately. For instance, do not send "R," meaning you have received everything correctly, and then ask for repeats like "AA" (all after) or "AB" (all before).

Interference Problems

If your net experiences interference, the NCS has several options. If the interference is coming from adjacent or co-channel stations who may be unaware of the emergency net, the NCS should politely inform them of the net and ask for their cooperation. Alternately, the NCS might ask an HF net to move over a few kHz. If the problem cannot be resolved in this manner, each net should have one or more alternate frequencies that it can move to as required. If possible, the frequencies themselves should not be published or mentioned on the air.

Never discuss, acknowledge, or try to speak with an intentionally interfering station. Experience has proven that this only encourages the offender. If the interference is making communication difficult, simply announce to the net that everyone should move to the alternate frequency and sign off.

If the intentional interference persists, the Net Manager or NCS can contact an elected League official or an Official Observer Station, and ask that the FCC be notified of the interference. In some cases they may be able to track down and contact the responsible station.

Reference links:

For information about **ARRL Public Service Communications**, please see www.arrl.org/FandES/field/pscm/index.html or *The Public Service Communications Manual*

Review:

As the net's "ringmaster," the NCS operator is responsible for keeping the net operating smoothly and assuring that messages are sent in order of priority. A off-site backup or alternate NCS operator is essential for long-running nets in the event of equipment failure or operator fatigue.

Net member stations should monitor the net continuously whenever possible, as well as maintaining contacts with the served agency's staff at that location. Liaison stations pass traffic between two different nets, sometimes only in one direction, and sometimes in both directions. Bulletin stations transmit bulletin messages from the served agency to the net.

CW nets can move messages very quickly and accurately, but slightly different procedures are used than with phone. Packet radio doesn't use a conventional net format due to its automatic nature, and is well suited to handling large volumes of traffic, or highly detailed and lengthy messages.

Student activities:

1. List the advantage and disadvantage of each of the following modes for an emcomm operation:
   A. *Voice net*
   B. *CW net*
   C. *Packet*
   D. *Non-Packet Digital*

2. What are the major topics found in ARRL's FSD-218?

Share all your answers with your mentor.

Questions:

1. Which of the following best describes the responsibilities of the NCS in an emcomm operation?
A. The NCS is responsible for all aspects of the emcomm operation.
B. The NCS is responsible for station check in.
C. The NCS is responsible for all aspects of the net's operation.
D. The NCS is responsible for writing the net script.

2. As an acting "fill in" NCS, which of the following practices would you avoid?
A. Try to run an existing net much as the previous NCS did.
B. Handle messages in order of precedence: Emergency-Priority-Welfare.
C. Keep notes as you go along: do not let your log fall behind.
D. Ask stations to pass messages on the main net frequency whenever possible.

3. Which of the following is true of a liaison station?
A. The liaison station mainly relays bulletins authorized by the served agency to all stations on the net.
B. A liaison station passes messages only on a pre-set schedule.
C. A liaison station handles only one-way traffic.
D. A liaison station passes messages between two nets.

4. Packet modes include which of the following groups?
A. FM packet, HF packet and PACTOR.
B. HF packet, PACTOR and PSK31.
C. PACTOR, PSK31 and RTTY.
D. PSK31, RTTY and PACTOR.

5. You are the NCS of a net involved in an emcomm operation and you notice that some other station is intentionally interfering with your net. Which of the following represents your best course of action?

A. Shut down the net and go home.

B. Address the interfering station directly and inform them of the error of their ways.

C. Move the net to an alternate frequency.

D. Contact the EOC and continue to operate.

Learning Unit 10

Special Events as Training Opportunities

Objective:

Emcomm groups frequently use public service event communication as training for emergency communication. This unit will help you to understand the similarities and differences between public service and emergency communication, and to get the most out of these events.

Student preparation required:

None

Information:

Public service events, such as walk and bike-a-thons, road races, marathons, and parades have a great deal in common with emergency communication, but a few differences as well.

Similarities to emcomm:
- Both often use the same equipment (mobile, portable and foot-mobile stations).
- Both can have similar network designs and use various modes.
- Both may require occasional or prolonged contact with fire, police or medical agencies.
- Pre-planning may involve more than one agency, especially if communications may need to be relayed to and from public safety agencies.
- Often uses similar tactical net operations.
- Technical challenges may be similar.
- Event occurs in "real time," and problems must be solved as they happen.
- Not everything is predictable.
- Emcomm jump kits usually have everything needed for public service operations.

Differences from emcomm:
- Public service events are scheduled - emergencies are not.
- Public service does not require activation by an emergency management agency.
- Does not use an "activation system" and related deployment plans.
- Public service events involve only a single served agency in most cases. Many emergencies involve serving several different agencies.
- Personnel can be recruited, confirmed, and scheduled in advance.
- Network designs can be planned and tested in advance.
- Logistical problems can be solved before the event.
- Operator IDs and security checks are not usually required except for large events.
- Formal messages are seldom needed.

- No need to interface with long distance traffic nets (NTS).

Training Objectives

Before your group can integrate any training objectives into a public service event communication plan, you must first meet the needs of the served agency. The network structure (directed or informal) can be chosen based on the needs of the event, or if it does not matter, on the training needs of the emcomm group.

Once those needs are met, your group might consider using different modes for primary or backup communication. For instance, you could try both PSK31 and packet radio for relaying the numbers of the runners who have passed your checkpoint, and see which is more effective. Your net can be more formal than otherwise required, and some messages could be passed in NTS or served agency formats. If you have the resources, it might be a good time to experiment with Amateur television (ATV) or Automatic Packet Reporting System (APRS).

For individual radio operators, it is a good time to test portable and mobile equipment, as well as hone operating skills in the net environment. Simple events are a good place to allow a trainee NCS to run the net.

Volunteer Identification

Volunteer communicators should be readily identifiable, usually by some piece of clothing. Hats, T-shirts, and vests are commonly used. This will allow event officials to find you when needed, and provides the additional benefit of exposure to the public. Vehicles can be identified with magnetic signs such as those for ARES available from the ARRL and others.

Special Training Sessions

Certain public service events are so large and complex that volunteers must be recruited from a wide area. This may mean that the sponsoring group will not know many of them, or the level of training and expertise they bring. In this case, the sponsoring emcomm group may offer one or more event-specific training sessions. The Boston and New York Marathons are two well-known events where this is done each year.

Types of Events and Their Unique Requirements

Parades: Parades can vary in size and complexity. Small parades can be rather relaxed events; the largest parades can rival major disasters in the level of effort required.
Operations: Often needs to show up ahead of parade time to assist in the organization of the parade. Multiple fixed or mobile operating locations are likely. In an area with tall buildings or hills, or if the parade route is longer than one mile, use high-powered mobile rather than hand-held radios. Long routes in difficult areas may require repeaters to provide end-to-end coverage. Some mobile stations or bicycles may be

needed, and some operators may need to ride in or on floats. Operators may need to "shadow" key parade officials. Stations may be dismissed or moved to another location once the end of the parade passes their location.

Messages: Nearly all of the traffic is tactical and informal in nature. There is often a need to relay changes in the parade line-up (participating or non-participating parade units, order of the parade) from the starting position to all review stands announcing the parade units, traffic and crowd problems, and medical emergencies. It is helpful to have an EMT with an ambulance dispatch radio at the communication command post for expediting the response to medical emergencies.

Logistics: Operators should be self-contained for food and water needs if possible to reduce the need to leave your assigned post. Restrooms may be accessible at restaurants and other establishments along the parade route. The organizers may place portable toilet facilities along the route and in the mustering area.

Marathons, Fun Runs, Bike-a-thons:

Similar to parades, although the course and event duration can be longer.

Operations: May require more fixed stations with higher-powered base or mobile radios. Roving stations may be needed to monitor the entire course, and their locations tracked. Roving stations may be in either personal or event vehicles, such as busses, trucks, vans, or ambulances. Longer routes may require a repeater, or multiple nets with liaison stations. The last competitor can be tracked so that the NCS knows when each station can be closed.

Messages: Communications are usually between aid station or checkpoint staff, and the start and finish line officials. The first several competitors are often tracked and their progress relayed to event officials. Re-supply deliveries for aid stations are coordinated. Calls are made for event vehicles to pick up exhausted or injured participants. Ambulances may be called for more serious injuries. Additional or replacement volunteers may be requested and dispatched as needed.

Logistics: Some stations may need to operate in unfamiliar vehicles, requiring magnetic mount antennas and special power connections. Aid stations are usually spaced throughout the course offering water, first aid and transportation. Portable toilet facilities may or may not be available.

Car Road Rallies, Endurance Races:

These events can have very long courses, sometimes stretching for hundreds of miles.

Operations: Multiple repeaters and nets are often required, and HF operations on 75m and 40m may be required.

Messages: Participants may be tracked and their positions reported to the start and finish lines, and to participant's support crews. Missing participants may need to be located, supplies and repair parts arranged for, tow trucks and ambulances requested.

Logistics: Some operators may need to be fully self-sufficient, especially with regard to food, water and toilet facilities. Some stations may need to operate in unfamiliar vehicles, requiring magnetic mount antennas and special power connections. Backup and renewable power sources may be needed for long-term use at isolated checkpoints.

Sporting events, Block Parties and Community Gatherings
Operations: Usually have a higher percentage of pedestrian mobile stations deployed to observe and assist the crowd.
Messages: Traffic is usually routed to and from the communications command post and to outside agencies as needed.
Logistics: Most of these events will have adequate access to food water and toilet facilities, and power for operating radios and charging batteries.

Reference links:
- For information about **ARRL Public Service Communications**, please see www.arrl.org/FandES/field/pscm/index.html or *The Public Service Communications Manual*.
- For specific information on **ARES**, see the ARRL ARES Field Resources Manual (.pdf file)

Review:

Despite certain differences from emergencies, public service events offer an excellent communication training opportunity. Depending on the size and complexity of the event, much of the same communication infrastructure is needed for either. The needs of the served agency come first, but if those are taken care of your group can use the event to experiment with new or different modes and bands, train new NCS operators, and hone net operating skills.

Student activities:

1. Outline a communication plan for a three-mile fun run on a straight course that will introduce or test an emcomm skill or procedure.

2. In what ways would your three-mile fun run communication plan have to be modified for a 26-mile marathon?

Share your answers with your mentor.

Questions:

1.Which of the following applies to public service events, but not emcomm operations?
A. Technical challenges arise.
B. Not everything is predictable.
C. Problems occur in "real time" and must be solved as they happen.
D. Logistics and personnel schedules can be arranged in advance.

2. Which of the following represents a <u>similarity</u> between public service events and emcomm operations?
A. Network designs can be planned and tested in advance.
B. You can put the event on your calendar in advance.
C. Logistic problems can be solved before the event.
D. Personnel can be arranged for in advance.

3. Before integrating emcomm training objectives into a public service event, what must first be accomplished?
A. Portable and mobile equipment must be tested.
B. The needs of the served agency must be met.
C. The use of Amateur Television (ATV) and Automatic Packet Reporting (APRS) must be explored.
D. Different modes of primary and backup communication must be considered.

4. Which of the following is true of parades?
A. They do not vary in their complexity.
B. Radio traffic in support of parades is nearly always formal.
C. Only fixed, rather than mobile operating stations, are appropriate.
D. Longer routes in difficult areas may require the use of repeaters.

5. Which of the following is true of marathons, fun runs and Bike-A-Thons?
A. They never require more than one net.
B. They never require the use of repeaters.
C. Every competitor must be tracked.
D. They may require roving stations.

Learning Unit 11

The Incident Command System

Objectives:

Following completion of this Learning Unit, you will understand the Incident Command System (ICS) concept, and how it is used to coordinate and unify multiple agencies during emergencies.

Student preparation required:

None

Information:

This lesson is a summary of ICS and its relationship to emcomm, and not a complete description of its various forms and uses. Please see the *Resource links* section at the end of the lesson for information on formal ICS training opportunities.

The History of ICS

In the early 1970s, a disorganized and ineffective multi-agency response to a series of major wildland fires in Southern California prompted municipal, county, state, and federal fire authorities to form an organization known as Firefighting Resources of California Organized for Potential Emergencies (FIRESCOPE). California authorities had found that a lack of coordination and cooperation between the various responding agencies resulted in over-lapping efforts, and gaps in the overall response. Many specific problems involving multi-agency responses were identified by FIRESCOPE. These included poor overall organization, ineffective communication between agencies, lack of accountability, and the lack of a well-defined command structure.

Their efforts to address these difficulties resulted in the development of the original Incident Command System. Although developed for wildland fires, the system ultimately evolved into an "all-risk" system, appropriate for all types of fire and non-fire emergencies.

There are other versions of the ICS in use. But the Incident Command System (ICS), as developed by the National Fire Academy (NFA), has been widely recognized as a model tool for the command, control, and coordination of resources and personnel at the scene of an emergency. Most fire, police, and other agencies around the country use it. Various federal laws for all hazardous material incidents, and in other situations by many states and local laws now require the use of the ICS. The ICS has also been adopted for use in many other countries.

What is the ICS?

The Incident Command System is a management tool designed to bring multiple responding agencies, including those from different jurisdictions, together under a single overall command structure. Before the use of the ICS became commonplace, various agencies responding to a disaster often fought for control, duplicated efforts, missed critical needs, and generally reduced the potential effectiveness of the response. Under ICS, each agency recognizes one "lead" coordinating agency and person, will handle one or more tasks that are part of a single over-all plan, and interact with other agencies in defined ways.

The Incident Command System is based upon simple and proven business management principles. In a business or government agency, managers and leaders perform the basic daily tasks of planning, directing, organizing, coordinating, communicating, delegating, and evaluating. The same is true for the Incident Command System, but the responsibilities are often shared between several agencies. These tasks, or *functional areas* as they are known in the ICS, are performed under the overall direction of a single Incident Commander (IC) in a coordinated manner, even with multiple agencies and across jurisdictional lines.

What the ICS is *not*

Many people who have not studied the full details of the Incident Command System have a variety of erroneous perceptions about what the system means to them and their agencies. To set the record straight, the Incident Command System **is not**:

- A fixed and unchangeable system for managing an incident.
- A means to take control or authority away from agencies or departments that participate in the response.
- A way to subvert the normal chain of command within a department or agency.
- Always managed by the fire department.
- Too big and cumbersome to be used in small, everyday events.
- Restricted to use by government agencies and departments.

The ICS Structure

The Incident Command System has two interrelated parts. They are "management by objectives," and the "organizational structure."

Management by objectives:

Four essential steps are used in developing the response to every incident, regardless of size or complexity:

- Understand the policies, procedures, and statutes that affect the official response.
- Establish incident objectives (the desired outcome of the agencies' efforts).

- Select appropriate strategies for cooperation and resource utilization.
- Apply tactics most likely to accomplish objectives (assign the correct resources and monitor the results).

The complexity of the incident will determine how formally the "management by objectives" portion will be handled. If the incident is small and uncomplicated, the process can be handled by verbal communication between appropriate people. As the incident and response become more complex, differences between the individual agencies' or departments' goals, objectives, and methods will need to be resolved in writing.

Organizational structure:

The ICS supports the creation of a flexible organizational structure that can be modified to meet changing conditions. Under the ICS, the one person in charge is always called the "Incident Commander" (IC). In large responses, the IC may have a "General Staff" consisting of the Information, Safety, and Liaison Officers. In a smaller incident, the IC may also handle one, two, or all three of these positions, if they are needed at all.

Various other tasks within the ICS are subdivided into four major operating sections: Planning, Operations, Logistics, and Finance/Administration. Each operating section has its own "chief," and may have various "task forces" working on specific goals. The Logistics section handles the coordination of all interagency communication infrastructures involved in the response, including Amateur Radio.

These operating sections may be scaled up or down, depending on the needs of the situation. In a small, single agency response, the IC may handle many or all functions. As the size and complexity of a response increase, and as other agencies become involved, the various tasks can be re-assigned and sub-divided.

For instance, if the only responding agency is the fire department, communications will be handled according to existing department policies. If the incident expands, more agencies become involved, and other communication assets are required, a Logistics Chief may handle communication decisions along with other tasks, or assign the job to a "communication task force leader" as his own workload increases.

The Incident Commander: The initial IC is usually the most senior on-scene officer from the first responding agency. The IC is responsible for the management of the incident and starts the process by helping setting initial incident objectives, followed by an "Incident Plan" (IP). In a small incident, the IC may do all the ICS functions without aid, but in a larger incident, they will usually delegate responsibilities to others. The IC still has overall responsibility for the incident, regardless of any duties delegated.

The persons filling certain ICS positions may change several times during an incident as the needs of the response change. For instance, in the early stages of a hazardous materials spill, the Incident Commander may be a fire department officer. As the Coast

Guard or other federal agency arrives to begin cleanup efforts, one of their officers will become the Incident Commander.

> The organizational charts below depict a full-scale ICS organization. For smaller responses, many of these functions may not be needed, or will be performed by the IC or others on his staff in addition to other duties.

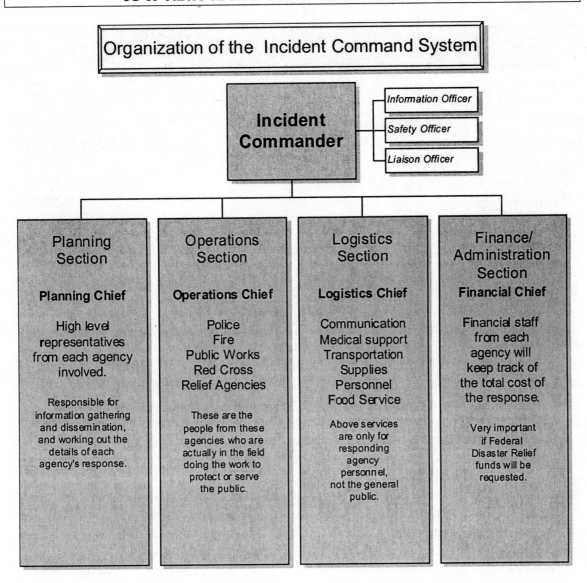

Organization of the Incident Command System

Incident Commander

- Information Officer
- Safety Officer
- Liaison Officer

Planning Section

Planning Chief

High level representatives from each agency involved.

Responsible for information gathering and dissemination, and working out the details of each agency's response.

Operations Section

Operations Chief

Police
Fire
Public Works
Red Cross
Relief Agencies

These are the people from these agencies who are actually in the field doing the work to protect or serve the public.

Logistics Section

Logistics Chief

Communication
Medical support
Transportation
Supplies
Personnel
Food Service

Above services are only for responding agency personnel, not the general public.

Finance/Administration Section

Financial Chief

Financial staff from each agency will keep track of the total cost of the response.

Very important if Federal Disaster Relief funds will be requested.

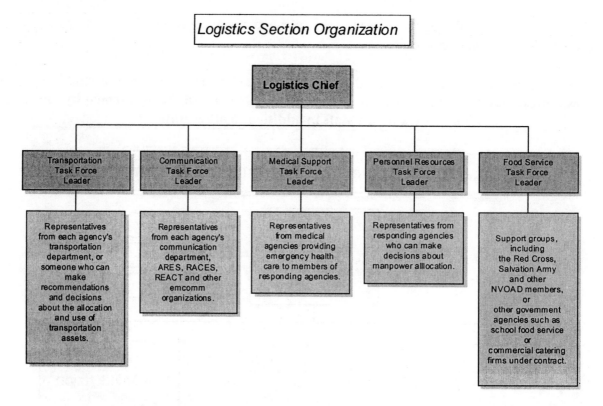

How does an emcomm group "fit in" to the ICS

The relationship of an emcomm group to the ICS structure will vary with the specific situation. If your group is providing internal communication support to only one responding agency, and has no need to communicate with other agencies that are part of the ICS, you may not have any part in the ICS structure itself except through your served agency. If your group is tasked with handling inter-agency communications, or serves more than one agency's internal communication needs, it is likely your group will have a representative on the Logistics Section's "communication task force."

In certain situations, an emcomm group might serve one or more agencies simultaneously. As the responsibility for managing the incident shifts from one agency to another, the emcomm group's mission may shift to assisting the new lead agency, or simply end. In some cases, your group might begin by supporting your own served agency, and end up supporting a new and unfamiliar agency. The choice of whether to use your emcomm group's services may be made by the served agency, Communications Task Force leader, Logistics Chief, or Incident Commander, depending on the specific situation and ICS structure in use.

Reference links:

Basic Incident Command System course: http://training.fema.gov/EMIWeb/is195.htm

Review:

The ICS is a management tool that preserves the command structure of each responding agency, while bringing them all together under a common plan and leader. Emcomm groups often operate as part of the Logistics section of the ICS. If the emcomm group serves the internal communication needs of only one agency, it may not be a formal part of the ICS structure.

Student Activities:

1. Contact a leader of your local emcomm group. Ask the leader:
   A if the emcomm group is affiliated with a specific agency;
   B. if there is a local, planned ICS structure and if so;
   C. how the emcomm group fits into the local ICS structure.

2. Contact a leader of your local emcomm group. Ask the leader if the emcomm group has ever been activated. If so, what were the lessons learned from operating with local agencies?

3. Suppose that during an emergency activation, you find yourself to be the leader of the local emcomm group. To which agency would you report? To whom within the agency would you report? What would your duties be as leader of the emcomm group?

Questions:

1. What do the letters "ICS" stand for?
A. International Correspondence School
B. Incident Command System
C. Institutional Control System
D. Internal Control Sequence

2. What is ICS?
A. A management tool for coordinating the resources of several agencies within a single command structure.
B. A fixed and unchangeable system for managing an incident.
C. A means of subverting the normal command structure within an agency or department.
D. A management system restricted to use by government agencies and departments.

3. The ICS has two interrelated parts. What are they?
A. A mission statement and management objectives
B. Management by objectives and organizational structure.
C. Organizational structure and a financial plan.
D. A financial plan and an operational plan.

4. Aside from the Incident Commander, there are four other major operating sections within an ICS. What are they?
A. Planning, Operations, Logistics and Public Relations
B. Personnel, Planning, Operations and Finance/Administration
C. Planning, Operations, Logistics, and Finance/Administration
D. Payroll, Finance/Administration, Logistics and Operations.

5. How does an emcomm group fit into an ICS?
A. The emcomm group always serves within the Logistics area
B. The emcomm group may or may not be a formal part of the ICS structure.
C. The emcomm group always serves the Task Force leader directly.
D. The emcomm group always serves the Incident Commander directly.

6. Which of the following is NOT one of the essential steps in developing a response to an incident?
A. Understanding the policies, procedures and statutes that affect the official response.
B. Establish incident objectives
C. Select appropriate strategies for cooperation and resource utilization
D. Conduct evaluation of operations immediately following the incident.

Learning Unit 12

Preparing for Deployment

Objective:

In this lesson we will discuss the steps an emcomm volunteer should take to be ready to respond quickly, and be fully prepared to handle their emcomm assignment.

Student preparation required:

None

Information:

Prepared for What?

Remember the Boy Scout motto, "Be Prepared"? Nearly one hundred years ago, a young British Boy Scout asked Sir Robert Baden-Powell, the founder of Scouting, what exactly it was he should be prepared for. B-Ps famous answer was, "Why, for any old thing, of course!"

The same should be true of emcomm volunteers. You never know what challenges an emergency situation will offer. You might have AC power, or just the batteries you bring along. Safe drinking water may be available, or you may have only your canteen. Sometimes you can find out in advance what sort of conditions are likely for your assignment, but many times no one will know – particularly during the early stages of an emergency.

Being prepared for an emergency communication deployment involves a wide range of considerations, including radio equipment, clothing and personal gear, food and water, information, and specialized training. No two deployments are the same, and each region offers its own specific challenges. What is appropriate for rural Minnesota in January probably won't work for urban southern California in any season. In this Learning Unit, our goal is to help you think about ways to be prepared for your particular situation. We cannot provide all the answers, but we can help you to ask the correct questions. Specific equipment choices are covered in the next Learning Unit.

Jump Kits

The last thing you should need to do when a call for assistance comes is think of and locate all the items you might need. Any experienced emergency responder knows how important it is to keep a kit of the items they need ready to go at a moment's notice. This is often called a "jump kit."

Without a jump kit, you will almost certainly leave something important at home, or bring items that will not do the job. Gathering and packing your equipment at the last moment also wastes precious time. It is important to think through each probable deployment ahead of time, and the range of situations you might encounter. Here are a few basic questions you will need to answer:

- Which networks will you need to join, and what equipment will you need to do so?
- Will you need to be able to relocate quickly, or can you bring a ton of gear?
- Will you be on foot, or near your vehicle?
- Is your assignment at a fixed location or will you be mobile?
- How long might you be deployed - less than 48 hours, up to 72 hours, or even a week or more?
- Will you be in a building with reliable power and working toilets, or in a tent away from civilization?
- What sort of weather or other conditions might be encountered?
- Where will food and water come from? Are sanitary facilities available?
- Will there be a place to sleep?
- Do you need to plan for a wide variety of possible scenarios, or only a few?

Other questions may occur to you based on your own experience. If you are new to emcomm or the area, consult with other members of your group for their suggestions.

Most people seem to divide jump kits into two categories: one for deployments under 48 hours, and one for up to 72 hours. For deployments longer than 72 hours, many people will just add more of the items that they will use up, such as clothing, food, water, and batteries. Others may add a greater range of communication options and backup equipment as well.

Everyone has their own favorite list of items to keep in a jump kit. While preparing this course material we looked at quite a few. Some were detailed, others more general. Some responders have more than one kit for different types of deployments. You will need to develop your own, suited to your own needs, but here is a general list to help you get started. Depending on your situation, you may not need some of the items on this list, or you may need special items not listed.

Jump Kit Idea List
- Something to put it in – one or more backpacks, suitcases, plastic storage tubs, etc.
- Package individual items in zip lock bags or plastic kitchen containers

Radios and Accessories
- Handheld VHF or dual-band radio (some people also like to bring a spare)
- Spare rechargeable batteries for handhelds
- Alkaline battery pack for handhelds
- Alkaline batteries
- Speaker mic and earphone for handhelds

- Battery chargers, AC and DC for handhelds
- Mobile VHF or dual-band radio
- HF radio
- Multi-band HF antenna, tuner, heavy parachute cord
- Gain antennas and adapters (roll-up J-Pole, mobile magnetic mount, etc)
- Coaxial feed lines, jumpers
- Ground rod, pipe clamp, and wire
- AC power supplies for VHF.UHF mobile and HF radios, accessories
- Large battery source for VHF/UHF mobile and HF radios, with charger
- All related power, data, audio, and RF cables and adapters
- Small repair kit: hand tools, multi-meter, connectors, adapters, fuses, key parts
- Materials for improvisation: wire, connectors, small parts, insulators, duct tape, etc.
- Photocopies of manuals for all equipment
- Headphones, for noisy areas and privacy
- Specialized gear for packet, ATV or other modes
- Multi-band scanner, weather radio
- Personal cell phone, pager, spare batteries and chargers
- Pencils, legal pads, pencil sharpener

Personal Gear
- Clothing for the season, weather, and length of deployment
- Toilet kit: soap, razor, deodorant, comb, toilet paper
- Foul weather or protective gear, warm coats, hats, etc. as needed
- Sleeping bag, closed-cell foam pad, pillow, ear plugs
- High energy snacks
- Easily prepared dried foods that will store for long periods
- Eating and cooking equipment if needed
- Water containers, filled before departure
- First aid kit, personal medications and prescriptions for up to one week
- Money, including a large quantity of quarters for vending machines, tolls, etc.
- Telephone calling card

Information
- ID cards and other authorizations
- Frequency lists and net schedules
- Maps, both street and topographic
- Key phone numbers, email and internet addresses
- Contact information for other members in your group, EC, DEC, SEC, and others
- Copy of emergency plans
- Resource lists: who to call for which kinds of problems
- Log sheets, message forms

Operating Supplies
- Outgoing message forms or sheets to compose messages
- Incoming message forms. (Some operators copy the message onto scratch paper, and then transcribe it cleanly onto the incoming message form. Some groups use one form for both incoming and outgoing messages.)
- Log sheets
- Standard forms used by the served agency
- Letter or legal notepads
- Sticky notes
- Paper clips and rubber bands
- Blank envelopes

Sub-Dividing Your Kits

You may want to divide your jump kit into smaller packages. Here are some ideas:
- Quick deployment kit: hand-held radio kit, personal essentials, in a large daypack
- VHF/UHF, HF kits for fixed locations
- Accessory and tool kit
- Emergency power kit
- Short and long term personal kits in duffel bags
- Field kitchen and food box in plastic storage tubs
- Field shelter kit (tents, tarps, tables, chairs, battery/gas lights) in plastic storage tubs

You may not want to pre-pack some items for reasons of expense or shelf life. Keep a checklist of these items in your jump kit so that you will remember to add them at the last minute.

Pre-Planning

When the time comes, you need to know where to go, and what to do. Having such information readily available will help you respond more quickly and effectively. It will not always be possible to know these things in advance, particularly if you do not have a specific assignment. Answering the following basic questions may help.
- Which frequency should you check in on initially? Is there a "backup" frequency?
- If a repeater is out of service, which simplex frequency is used for the net?
- Which nets will be activated first?
- Should you report to a pre-determined location or will your assignment be made as needed?

Learn about any place to which you may be deployed to familiarize yourself with its resources, requirements, and limitations. For instance, if you are assigned to a particular shelter, you might ask your emcomm superiors to schedule a visit, or talk to others who are familiar with the site.

- Will you need a long antenna cable to get from your operating position to the roof?
- Are antennas permanently installed, or will you need to bring your own?
- Will you be in one room with everyone else, or in a separate room?
- Is there dependable emergency power to circuits at possible operating positions?
- Does the building have an independent and dependable water supply?
- Is there good cell phone or beeper coverage inside the building?
- Can you reach local repeaters reliably with only a rubber duck antenna, or do you need an antenna with gain?
- If the repeaters are out of service, how far can you reach on a simplex channel?
- Will you need a HF radio?

If you will be assigned to an EOC, school, hospital, or other facility with its own radio system in place, learn under what conditions you will be required or able to use it, where it is, and how it works. In addition to radios, consider copiers, computers, fax machines, phone systems and other potentially useful equipment.

Consider escape routes. If you could be in the path of a storm surge or other dangerous condition, know all the possible routes out of the area. If you will be stationed in a large building such as a school or hospital, find the fire exits, and learn which parking areas will be the safest for your vehicle.

Training & Education

This may sound a bit redundant since you are already taking this course, but it cannot be over-stressed – the more you know, the more effective and valuable you will be. If the served agency offers emcomm volunteers job-specific training in areas related to communication, take it. Your emcomm managers should help you to learn how the served agency's organization works. Learn their needs and how you can best meet them. Work within your own emcomm organization to get any additional training or information you might need.

For instance, The American Red Cross offers self-study or classroom courses in mass care, damage assessment, and other areas that either directly involve or depend upon effective communication. Many emergency management agencies offer additional training in areas such as radiological monitoring, sheltering, mass casualty response, and evacuation. The Federal Emergency Management Agency's Emergency Management Institute offers a wide range of courses, some of which may be related to your agency's mission.

Your own group may offer agency-specific training in message handling and net operations under emergency conditions. If your group has its own equipment, it should offer opportunities for members to become familiar with its setup and operation in the field. On your own, set up and test your personal equipment under field conditions to be sure it works as expected.

Participate in any drills or exercises offered in your area. Some are designed to introduce or test specific skills or systems, others to test the entire response. ARRL's Field Day and Simulated Emergency Test are two good nation-wide examples, but local organizations may have their own as well.

Reference links:

Federal Emergency Management Agency - Emergency Management Institute
More about preparation can be found in ARES Field Resources Manual (.pdf file)
American Red Cross – Newsletter article regarding training opportunities

Review:

Pre-planning and physical preparation are essential to an effective and timely emergency response. Know in advance where are you are going, and what you will do when you get there. Keep a stocked and updated "jump kit" ready to go at a moments notice. Be sure your kit is adequate for the types of deployments you are most likely to encounter. Information is as important as equipment. Keep updated lists of other volunteers and contact information, frequencies, and other resources on hand as well as copies of all emcomm pre-plans.

Student activities:

1. Create a jump kit list suitable for your area and assignment.
2. Make a list of contacts and resources to keep in your jump kit

Complete both tasks and share this information with your mentor.

Optional activities:

1. Go to the FEMA Emergency Management Institute website. List five offerings from the Emergency Management Institute that you feel might be useful to emergency volunteers in your area.

2. The American Red Cross Newsletter listed in the Resource Links of this lesson focuses on the importance of training for disaster workers.

A. According to the newsletter, what action must an individual take before participating in Red Cross sponsored disaster training?

B. Which of the training ideas posed within the newsletter would be valuable to members of an emcomm group?

Questions:

*1. Of the following, which is the **best** reason for preparing a jump kit in advance?*
A. You will not leave something important at home or waste valuable time.
B. You are spared the added expense of shopping for something after an emergency arises.
C. You can be fully rested on the day of the emergency.
D. You can test the batteries on your hand held VHF before leaving home.

2. Which of the following would you omit from a jump kit prepared for a 12-hour deployment?
A. Hand held VHF or dual band radio.
B. Spare rechargeable batteries for the hand held radio.
C. High energy snacks.
D. Camp cot and tent.

*3. Among the following, which are the **most** important items of information to include in your jump kit?*
A. ID cards and other authorizations.
B. Field cookbook.
C. Automobile repair manual.
D. Instruction book for your chain saw.

*4. Among the following, which is the **least** important item of personal gear to include in your jump kit?*
A. Frequency lists and net schedules.
B. Contact information for other members of your group, EC, DEC and SEC.
C. Key phone numbers, email and Internet addresses.
D. A deck of playing cards.

*5. If you are assigned in advance to a particular location for emcomm operations, what is the **least** important thing to know in advance?*
A. The escape routes from the facility itself.
B. The regular business hours maintained at the facility.
C. The availability of radio equipment at the facility.
D. The location of your operating position and the planned location of the antenna.

Learning Unit 13

Equipment Choices for Emergency Communication

Objective:

There is no one "best" set of equipment that will ensure success for every assignment, but the principles outlined in this Learning Unit will help you make intelligent choices.

Student Preparation Required:

None

Information:

Transceivers

VHF/UHF:

The most universal choice for emcomm is a dual band FM 35-50 watt mobile transceiver. Radios in this class are usually rugged and reliable, and can operate at reasonably high duty cycles, although an external cooling fan is always a good idea. Handheld transceivers should be used only when extreme portability is needed, such as when "shadowing" an official, or when adequate battery or other DC power is not available. Handheld radios should not be relied upon to operate with a high duty-cycle at maximum power, since they can overheat and fail.

Both portable and mobile dual-band radios can be used to monitor more than one net, and some models allow simultaneous reception on more than one frequency on the *same* band (Sometimes known as "dual watch" capability). Some mobiles have separate external speaker outputs for each band. For high traffic locations, such as a Net Control or Emergency Operations Center, a separate radio for each net is a better choice since it allows both to be used simultaneously by different operators. (Antennas must be adequately separated to avoid "de-sensing.")

Many dual-band transceivers also offer a "cross-band repeater" function, useful for linking local portables with distant repeaters, or as a quickly deployable hill-top repeater. True repeater operation is only possible if all other mobile and portable stations have true dual-band radios. Some so-called "dual" or "twin" band radios do not allow simultaneous or cross-band operation – read the specifications carefully before you purchase one.

HF:

Operation from a generator equipped Emergency Operations Center can be done with an AC powered radio, but having both AC and DC capability ensures the ability to operate under all conditions. Most 12 Volt HF radios fall in either the 100-watt or QRP (less than

5 watts) categories. Unless power consumption is extremely important, 100-watt variable output radios should be used. This gives you the ability to overcome noise at the receiving station by using high power, or to turn it down to conserve battery power when necessary.

Do not use DC to AC inverters to power HF radios. Most use a high-frequency conversion process that generates significant broad-spectrum RF noise at HF frequencies that is difficult to suppress. Direct DC powering is more efficient in any case.

Radio Receiver Performance:

For radios on all bands, several aspects of a radio receiver's performance can affect its suitability for emcomm. These include sensitivity (ability to receive weak signals), selectivity (ability to reject signals on adjacent frequencies), and intermodulation rejection (ability to prevent undesired signals from mixing within the receiver and causing interference). If you are inexperienced at comparing radio specifications, be sure to ask for guidance from another with more experienced, ham. An in-depth discussion of radio performance specifications is beyond the scope of this course.

When operating near public service and business radio transmitters, a FM receiver's "intermodulation rejection" is important. Mobile radios generally have better intermodulation rejection than handheld radios, but you should review each individual radio's specifications. External intermodulation (bandpass) filters are available, but they add to the expense, complexity, size, and weight of the equipment. Bandpass filters will also prevent you from using a broadband radio to monitor public service frequencies. Some older "ham bands only" FM mobile radios have better front-end filtering than newer radios with broadband receive capability, making them more immune to intermodulation and adjacent channel interference.

Receiver filters are important for effective HF operation. Choose appropriate filters for the types of operations you are most likely to use, including CW, RTTY, and phone.

Digital Signal Processing (DSP) may be the single most important filtering feature available. Internal or external DSP circuits can allow clear reception of signals that might not otherwise be possible in situations with heavy interference.

"Noise blankers" are used to reduce impulse noise from arcing power lines, vehicle and generator ignition systems, and various other sources. While most all HF radios have some form of noise blanker, some work better than others. Test your radio in suitably noisy environments before designating it for emcomm use.

Antennas

VHF/UHF:

A good antenna, mounted as high as possible, is more important than high transmitter power. Not only does it provide gain to both the transmitter and receiver, but a higher gain antenna may also allow output power to be reduced, thus prolonging battery life. In relatively flat terrain, use a mast-mounted single or dual-band antenna with at least 3dBd gain. If you are operating in a valley, the low angle of radiation offered by a gain antenna may actually make it difficult to get a signal out of the valley. Low or "unity" gain antennas have "fatter" radiation lobes and are better suited for this purpose. Unity gain J-poles are rugged, inexpensive and easily built. For directional 2m coverage with about 7 dB gain, a three or four element yagi can be used. Collapsible and compact antennas of this type are readily available. For permanent base station installations, consider a more rugged commercial 2-way colinear antenna, such as the well-known "Stationmaster" series. Most 2m versions will also perform well on 70cm. Commercial open dipole array antennas will work well for a single band, and are more rugged than a fiberglass radome encased colinear antenna.

A magnetic mount mobile antenna is useful for operating in someone else's vehicle. They can also be used indoors by sticking them to any steel surface, such as filing cabinets, beams, or ductwork, even up side down.

Hand-held radio antennas, known as "rubber duckies," have *negative* gain. Use at least a ¼ wave flexible antenna for most operations, and consider a telescoping 5/8-wave antenna for long-range use in open areas where the extra length and lack of flexibility will not be a problem. "Roll-up J-pole" antennas made from 300 ohm television twin-lead wire can be tacked up on a wall or hoisted into a tree with heavy-duty string. In addition to unity gain, the extra height can make a big difference. Even a mobile ½ wave magnetic mount antenna can be used with hand-helds when necessary.

HF:

There is no single perfect antenna for HF operation. Your choice depends on the size and terrain of the area you need to cover, and the conditions under which you must install and use it.

For local operations (up to a few hundred miles), a simple dipole hung at a less than ¼ wavelength above the ground works well and is easy to deploy. This is known as a "Near Vertical Incidence Skywave" (NVIS) antenna. The signal is reflected almost straight up, then bounces off the ionosphere directly back downward. NVIS propagation works best on 40 meters during the day, switching to 80 meters around sunset.

An antenna tuner is necessary for most portable wire antennas, (especially for NVIS antennas), and is a good idea for any HF antenna. The antenna's impedance will vary with its height above ground and proximity to nearby objects, which can be a real problem with expedient installations. An automatic tuner is desirable, since it is faster and easier to use, and many modern radios have one built in. Include a ground rod, clamps and cable in your kit since almost all radios and tuners require a proper ground in order to work efficiently.

For communication beyond 200 miles, a commercial trapped vertical may work, although it has no ability to reject interfering signals. Mobile whip antennas will also work, but with greatly reduced efficiency. The benefits of a mobile antenna are its size and durability.

Directional (beam) antennas offer the best performance for very wide area nets on 10 to 20 meters, since they maximize desired signals and reduce interference from stations in other directions. This ability may be critical in poor conditions. Beam antennas also have a number of limitations that should be considered. They are usually expensive, large, and difficult to store and transport. In field installations, they can be difficult to erect at the optimum height, and may not survive storm conditions. One strategy is to rely on easily installed and repaired wire dipole antennas until conditions allow the safe installation of beam antennas.

Feedline:

Feedline used at VHF and UHF should be low-loss foam dielectric coaxial cable. For short runs, RG-58 may be suitable, but for longer runs consider RG-8X or RG-213. RG-8X is an "in-between" size that offers less loss and greater power handling capability than RG-58 with far less bulk than RG-213. If you with to carry only one type of cable, RG-8X is the best choice.

On HF, the choice between coaxial cable and commercial (insulated – not open wire) "ladder" line will depend on your situation. Ladder line offers somewhat lower loss but more care must be taken in it's routing, especially in proximity to metal objects, or where people might touch it. Coaxial cable is much less susceptible to problems induced by routing near metal objects or other cables.

Operating Accessories

Headphones are useful anywhere, and are mandatory in many locations. Operators in an Emergency Operations Center or a Command Post where multiple radios are in use *must* use headsets. They are also beneficial in locations such as Red Cross shelters, to prevent disturbing residents and other volunteers trying to get some rest.

Some radios and accessory headsets provide a VOX (voice operated transmit) capability. During emcomm operations this should always be turned off and manual "push-to-talk" buttons used instead. Accidental transmissions caused by background noise and conversations can interrupt critical communications on the net.

As an alternative to VOX, consider using a desk or boom microphone and foot switch to key the transmitter. A microphone/headset combination and foot switch also works well.

Batteries

Battery power is critical for emcomm operations. AC power cannot usually be relied upon for any purpose, and portable operation for extended periods is common.

Batteries must be chosen to match the maximum load of the equipment, and the length of time that operation must continue before they can be recharged.

NiCd, NiMH, and LIon:

For handheld transceivers, the manufacturer determines the internal battery type. NiMH batteries store somewhat more energy than NiCd batteries for their size. Many smaller radios are using Lithium Ion (LIon) batteries, which have much higher power densities, without the so-called "memory effect" of NiCds. Many handhelds have optional AA alkaline battery cases, and are recommended emcomm accessories. Common alkaline batteries have a somewhat higher power density than NiCd batteries, are readily available in most stores, and may be all you have if you cannot recharge your other batteries. Most handheld radios will accept an external 13.8VDC power connection for cigarette lighter or external battery use. External batteries of any type can be used with a handheld, as long as the voltage and polarity are observed. Small gel cells and some battery packs intended for power tools and camcorders are all possibilities. For maximum flexibility, build a DC power cable for each of your radios, with suitable adapters for each battery type you might use.

Lead Acid:

There are three common types of lead-acid batteries: flooded (wet), VRLA (Valve Regulated Lead Acid), and SLA (Sealed Lead-Acid). Wet batteries can spill if tipped, but VRLA batteries use a gelled electrolyte or absorbtive fiberglass matt (AGM technology) and cannot spill. SLA batteries are similar to VRLA batteries, but can be operated in any position – even up-side down. All lead-acid batteries are quite heavy.

Lead acid batteries are designed for a variety of applications. "Deep-cycle" batteries are a better choice than common automotive (cranking) batteries, which are not designed to provide consistent power for prolonged periods, and will be damaged if allowed to drop below approximately 80% of their rated voltage. Deep cycle batteries are designed for specific applications and vary slightly in performance characteristics. For radio operation, the best choice would be one specified for UPS (uninterruptible power source) or recreational vehicle (RV) use. For lighting and other needs, a marine type battery works well. For best results, consult the manufacturer before making a purchase.

Sealed lead acid (SLA) or "gel cells," such as those used in alarm or emergency lighting systems, are available in smaller sizes that are somewhat lighter. These batteries are also the ones sold in a variety of portable power kits for Amateur Radio and consumer use. Typical small sizes are 2, 4, and 7Ah, but many sizes of up to more than 100Ah are available. SLA batteries should never be deeply discharged. For example, a 12 volt SLA battery will be damaged if allowed to drop below 10.5 volts. Excessive heat can damage SLA batteries. Storage and operaing temperatures in excess of 75 degrees F. will reduce the battery's life by half. Your car's trunk is not a good place to store them in warm weather. Cooler temperatures will extend the battery's life.

Battery "Power Budgeting":

The number of ampere/hours (AH – a rating of battery capacity) required, called a "power budget," can be roughly estimated by multiplying the radio's receive current by the number of hours of operation. Then adding the product of the transmit current multiplied by the estimated number of hours of transmission. For a busy net control station, the transmit current will be the determining factor because of the high duty cycle. For low activity stations, the receiver current will dominate. The value obtained from this calculation is only a rough estimate of the ampere/hours required. The AH rating of the actual battery should be up to 50% higher, due to variations in battery capacity and age.

Estimated 24-hour power budget example

Receive current: 1 amp x 24 hours = 24 AH
Transmit current: 8 amps x 6 hours = <u>48</u> AH (25% transmit duty cycle)
Total AH: 72 AH estimated actual consumption
Actual battery choice 72 x 1.5 = 108 AH

Chargers, Generators and Solar Power
Battery Chargers:

You should have two or more batteries so that one can be charging while another is in use.

NiCd and NiMH batteries:

The type of charger required depends on the battery – for instance, most NiCd chargers will also charge NiMH, but not LIon batteries. Several aftermarket "universal" chargers are available that can charge almost any battery available. A rapid-rate charger can ensure that you always have a fresh battery without waiting, although rapid charging can shorten a battery's overall lifespan.

Lead-acid batteries:

Always consult the battery's manufacturer for precise charging and maintenance instructions, as they can vary somewhat from battery to battery. It is best to slow-charge all batteries, since this helps avoid over-heating and extends their over-all life span. In general, automotive and deep cycle batteries can be charged with an automobile and jumper cables, an automotive battery charger, or any constant-voltage source. If a proper battery charger is not available, any DC power supply of suitable voltage can be used, but a heavy-duty isolation diode must be connected between the power supply and the battery. (This is important, since some power supplies have a "crowbar" overvoltage circuit, which short-circuits the output if the voltage exceeds a certain limit. If a battery is connected, the crowbar could "short-circuit" the battery with disastrous results.) The output voltage of the supply must be increased to compensate for the diode's voltage drop. Take a measurement at the battery to be sure. Wet batteries should be charged at about 14.5 volts, and VRLA batteries at about 14.0 volts. The charging current should not exceed 20% of the battery's capacity. For example, a 20-amp charger is the largest that should be used for a battery rated at approximately 100 Ah. Consult the battery's manufacturer for the optimum charging voltage and current whenever possible.

Deep cycle batteries do not normally require special charging procedures. However, manufacturers do recommend that you use a charger designed specifically for deep cycle batteries to get the best results and ensure long life.

SLA or "gel- cell" batteries must be charged slowly and carefully to avoid damage. All batteries produce hydrogen sulfide gas while recharging. Non-sealed batteries vent it out. SLA batteries do what is called "gas recombination." This means that the gas generated is "recombined" into the cells. SLA batteries actually operate under pressure, about 3 p.s.i. for most. If the battery is charged too quickly, the battery generates gas faster then it can recombine it and the battery over-pressurizes. This causes it to overheat, swell up, and vent, and can be dangerous and will permanently damage the battery.

The charging voltage must be kept between 13.8 and 14.5 volts. The time it takes for a SLA battery to recharge completely will depend on the amount of charge remaining in the battery. If the battery is only 25% discharged then it may recharge in a few hours. If the battery is discharged 50% or more, 18-24 hours may be required. A good rule of thumb is to keep the charging current level to no more than 1/3 its rated capacity. For example, if you have a 7Ah battery, you should charge it at no more than 2 amps.

Solar panels and charge controllers are readily available at increasingly lower costs. These provide yet another option for powering equipment in the field when weather and site conditions permit their use. When choosing solar equipment, consult with the vendor regarding the required size of panels and controller for your specific application.

DC to AC inverters. While direct DC power is more efficient and should be used whenever possible, inverters can be used for equipment that cannot be directly powered with 12VDC.

Not all inverters are suitable for use with radios, computers, or certain types of battery chargers. The best inverters are those with a "true sine-wave" output. Inverters with a "modified sine-wave" output may not operate certain small battery chargers, and other waveform-sensitive equipment. In addition, all "hi-frequency conversion" inverters generate significant RF noise if they are not filtered, both radiated and on the AC output. Test your inverter with your radios, power supplies, and accessories (even those operating nearby on DC) and at varying loads before relying upon it for emcomm use.

Effective filtering for VHF and UHF can be added rather simply (using capacitors on the DC input, and ferrite donuts on the AC output), but reducing HF noise is far more difficult. Inverters should be grounded when in operation, both for safety and to reduce radiated RF noise.

As a "quieter" alternative to an inverter, consider a mid-sized 12V computer UPS (uniterruptible power source). Smaller, square-wave UPS units are not designed for continuous duty applications, but larger true sine-wave units are. Most true sine-wave units use internal batteries, but with minor modifications can be used with external batteries. The larger commercial UPS units run on 24 or 48 volts, and require two or four external batteries in series. UPS units will have a limit on the number of depleted batteries they can re-charge, but there is no limit to the number of batteries that can be attached to extend operating time.

Generators are usually required at command posts and shelters, for lighting, food preparation, and other equipment. Radio equipment can be operated from the same or a separate generator, but be sure that multiple generators are bonded with a common ground system for safety. Not all generators have adequate voltage regulation, and shared generators can have widely varying loads to contend with. You should perform a test for regulation using a high-current power tool or similar rugged device before connecting sensitive equipment. A voltmeter should be part of your equipment any time auxiliary power sources are used.

Noise levels can be a concern with generators. Some are excessively noisy and can make radio operations difficult and increase fatigue. A noisy generator at a shelter can make it difficult for occupants to rest, and can result in increased levels of stress for already stressed people. Unfortunately, quieter generators also tend to be considerably more expensive. Consider other options such as placing the generator at a greater distance and using heavier power cables to compensate. Placing a generator far from a building can also prevent fumes from entering the building and causing carbon monoxide poisoning, an all-too-common problem with emergency generators.

Several other devices may be helpful when dealing with generators or unstable AC power sources. High quality surge suppressors, line voltage regulators, and power conditioners may help protect your equipment from defective generators. Variable voltage transformers ("Variacs" ™) can be useful to compensate for varying power conditions.

Power Connectors and Cables
There will be times you need to connect your equipment to someone else's power supply or battery. In these cases it is very helpful if everyone uses a standard power connector.

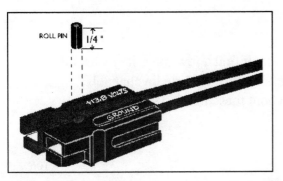

Anderson Power Pole

For a number of years, ARRL publications have suggested the use of the 12 amp Molex

1545 series connector (part numbers: male, 03-09-2022; female, 03-09-1022), also available from Radio Shack. While this connector is adequate for low power mobile radios, hand-helds, and accessories, it can overheat and fail when used with high power equipment and heavy duty cycles. An increasing number of groups have adopted the 30 amp Anderson Powerpole connector instead. Not only can the PowerPole handle much greater current, it is also capable of being plugged and unplugged many hundreds of times (operations) without deterioration.

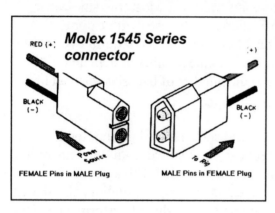

It is important to find out which connector is being used in your area. Just to be sure, always check the voltage and polarity of a power source before you plug your equipment in, since polarity conventions are not always followed.

All power cables should be properly fused in both the positive and negative leads. Fusing the negative leads helps to protect equipment from ground-fault currents.

When operating in a unfamiliar vehicle, you may need to use a "cigarette lighter plug" or "power point." Many of these receptacles are not able to deliver adequate current for mobile FM or HF radios operating at high power. Depending on the vehicle, the limit will be between 8 and 10 amperes. For this reason, it is important to know how much current your radio draws at different output power settings. A direct connection to the vehicle battery is almost always a better choice when feasible. This can be accomplished in most cases using a 15' power cable of adequate diameter, large battery clamps, and electrical tape to hold them in place on the battery terminals.

Equipment for Other Modes

If you plan to operate one of the digital modes (packet, APRS, AMTOR, PSK31, etc), then you will also need a computer and probably a TNC or computer sound card interface. Some newer radios have built-in TNC's. Be sure to identify all the accessories, including software and cables, needed for each mode. Include the power required to operate all of the radios and accessories when you are choosing your batteries and power supply. The internal battery in your laptop computer will probably not last long enough for you to complete your shift. Be prepared with an external DC power supply and cable, or a DC to AC inverter. If you need hard copy, then you will also need a printer, most of which are AC powered.

Scanners and Other Useful Equipment

In addition to your Amateur Radio equipment, you may find a few other items useful.
- Multi-band scanning radio (to monitor public service and media channels)
- FRS, GMRS or MURS hand-helds (more about these in LU 19)

- Cellular telephone (even an unregistered phone can be used to call 911)
- Portable cassette tape recorder with VOX (for logging, recording important events)
- AM/FM radio (to monitor media reports)
- Portable television (to monitor media reports)
- Weather Alert radio with "SAME" feature (to provide specific alerts without having to monitor the channel continuously)
- Laptop computer with logging or emcomm-specific packet software

Testing the Complete Station

After making your equipment selection (or beforehand if possible), field-test it under simulated disaster conditions. This is the fundamental purpose of the annual ARRL Field Day exercise in June, but any time will do. Operations such as Field Day can add the element of multiple, simultaneous operations on several bands and modes. Try to test all elements of your system together, from power sources to antennas, and try as many variations as possible. For instance, use the generator, then switch to batteries. Try charging batteries from the solar panels and the generator. Use the NVIS antenna while operating from batteries and then generator. This procedure will help reveal any interactions or interference between equipment and allow you to deal with them now - before proper operation becomes a matter of life and death.

Reference links:

Deep cycle battery tips http://www.interstatebatteryofdet.com/marinetips.html
Anderson PowerPole connectors http://www.andersonpower.com/
Molex 1545 Series connector data http://www.molex.com/products/power/std093p.html

Review:

All equipment chosen should be flexible and easy to use, rugged, and capable of being battery powered either directly or with a DC to AC inverter. Antennas should be compact, rugged, and easily erected. Directional or omni-directional gain antennas for VHF and UHF are essential in many locations, and the higher they are mounted, the better. Battery power is essential, as is a means of charging batteries. Testing equipment under field conditions before assigning it to emcomm uses ensures fewer surprises in an actual deployment. All equipment should be tested periodically for proper operation, and inpected for damage or deterioration.

Student activity:

Evaluate the equipment you now own to see if it is suitable for emcomm operation. Make a list of equipment you already own, and a second list of the items you will need to complete a basic emcomm package appropriate to your needs. Share the lists with your mentor.

Questions:

1. In considering power sources for HF radios, which of the following is true?
A. DC to AC inverters can be used to power HF radios.
B. Standard automotive batteries last longer than deep cycle batteries.
C. AC powered HF radios are suitable for all emcomm use.
D. Whenever possible, use deep cycle batteries to power HF radios.

2. In considering antennas for VHF/UHF radios, which is the best rule?
A. High transmitter power is more important than having a good antenna.
B. Transmitter power and antenna selection are equally important.
C. A good antenna is more important than high transmitter power.
D. If properly used, "rubber ducky" antennas can compensate for low transmitter power.

3. Beam antennas have many advantages. Which of the following is the best reason for selecting a beam antenna?
A. They are inexpensive and easy to transport.
B. They are easy to erect and very stable in storm conditions.
C. They are compact and easy to store.
D. They maximize desired signals and reduce interference from other stations.

4. Which of the following statements about battery charging is true?
A. The optimum charging voltage for lead acid batteries should be about two volts less than the battery's rated voltage.
B. The optimum charging voltage for 12-volt lead acid batteries should be about two volts more than the battery's rated voltage.
C. SLA or "gel cell" are ordinarily recharged very rapidly.
D. Deep cycle batteries require only a short time to recharge fully.

5. In comparing the 30 amp Anderson power pole connector with the 10 amp Molex connector, which of the following statements is true?
A. The Molex is better for high power applications.
B. The Molex is better for heavy duty cycles.
C. The Anderson handles only low power applications.
D. The Anderson is capable of being plugged and unplugged a greater number of times without deterioration.

Learning Unit 14

Emergency Activation

Objective:

This unit outlines some of the methods used to activate an emcomm group when an emergency occurs.

Student Preparation Required:

None.

Information:

How will I know?

The actual method by which emcomm volunteers are notified of activation will be determined locally, but this lesson outlines some of the most popular methods.

To begin with, you must be registered with a local emcomm group in advance in order to be on their notification list. "Last minute" volunteers are extremely difficult to integrate into an already confusing emergency response. Join the group well in advance of any emergency, get any training they offer, and be ready when a call comes.

The Activation Plan

Every emcomm group should have developed a formal, written plan with its served agency to activate their members when needed. Each member should know the plan and follow it closely. The plan should be developed in detail, and then reduced to a simple "checklist" that both served agency officials and emcomm managers can keep nearby at all times. It should detail the circumstances under which emcomm activation might occur, who will call whom, and the various methods that can be used to contact them. The checklist can also list the actual telephone numbers and other contact information for each individual listed in the order that it is to be used. This information should be verified and updated on a regular schedule.

Initial Notification by the Served Agency

In most cases, three or more members serve as "activation liaisons" to the served agency. When the emcomm volunteers are needed, it is one of these members who is called first. Never rely on a single point of contact. If that person is unavailable for any reason, the served agency should have one or more alternatives to try. They may be called by phone at work or at home, but the most reliable primary method is commercial radio paging (beepers). In the event that the paging system or an individual pager is not operating, the served agency should have all possible telephone numbers, including fax and mobile, and even email addresses.

Group Alerting Systems

Once a liaison has been notified, a number of groups alerting methods may be used. The most common ones are described below. No one method should be relied upon, since emergency conditions may render it useless. Commercial paging systems and ham repeaters might be off the air, phone lines down, and Internet service disrupted. Again, a written plan and checklist should be developed well in advance, and updated periodically.

Telephone Tree:

In this system, the liaison calls two members, who each call two other members and so on until the entire group has been notified. If any one person cannot be reached, the person calling must then call the members that person would have called had they been reached. This method insures that the "tree" is not broken. Messages should also be left on all answering machines and voice mailboxes.

Paging:

If commercial digital pagers are used, the liaison or someone he designates calls each member's pager telephone number and sends a specific numeric emcomm activation code. The code might indicate the six-digit frequency of a local repeater, followed by a three-digit "action" code (e.g.: 911 for an emergency, 000 for test). Some groups use a two-tone, POCSAG (digital), or similar paging signal on a local Amateur repeater with wide coverage, activating commercial voice or digital pagers that have been modified to monitor the repeater's frequency.

A low-cost method of "paging" a group using an Amateur repeater uses a specific Continuous Tone Coded Squelch System (CTCSS) tone. Members leave their radios turned on in the "CTCSS decode" mode when they are not actively listening to the repeater. When the correct CTCSS tone is turned on for emcomm activation, everyone can hear the transmissions. Since many newer radios include CTCSS decoding as a standard feature or low-cost option, this method is generally simple to implement. The tones may need to be generated by the repeater itself, since many repeaters will not "pass through" received tones. If the repeater is not operating, a mobile operating simplex on the repeater's output frequency from a high or central location can often work quite well.

Email:

While email might not immediately reach members anywhere they happen to be, it is a good backup method as long as it continues to function. Many people have full time high-speed Internet connections at home and the office, and most people check their email frequently. Someone who has otherwise been unreachable may check their email even several hours later, just as they might check an answering machine or voicemail box.

Self-Activation:

If you become aware of an incident or situation that might require the activation of your emcomm group, you should take immediate steps to make yourself available. Depending on your group's activation plan, this might mean monitoring the assigned net or served agency frequencies, or making contact with one or more appropriate persons in the emcomm group or served agency. SKYWARN members might also monitor National Weather Radio. Remember, if you are not specifically authorized to directly contact served agency personnel, do not do it. Know your plan and follow it.

I have been notified – Now what?

Your group's activation plan should tell each member what steps to take immediately after learning of an emcomm activation. In most cases, the first step should be to check in on a specific frequency or repeater. If a repeater is used as the primary gathering point for members, a back-up simplex frequency (the repeater's output frequency works well) should be specified in the event that the repeater is no longer operating. In other cases, some members may also have specific assignments. These might include making contact with the served agency, going directly to a specific location such as an EOC, or making certain preparations. If this is the case, it is still useful to have these members check into the "activation" net to let emcomm managers know that they have been reached and are responding.

One of the liaison stations should be available on the net to provide additional information and directions to members as they check in. If a member is pre-assigned to act as NCS for this "activation" net, that person should take over the task as soon as possible to free up the liaison to work with the served agency or take other action. Some groups simply have the first person signing on act as a temporary NCS until an assigned NCS checks in. Again, it is important to have more than one person assigned to take on the NCS duties in the event that anyone is unavailable.

En Route

While you are headed home to pick up your jump kit or other gear, or to your assigned location, there are several things you may need to do. Check into and continue to monitor the activation net for further information or instructions. Fill your vehicle with fuel and pick up any supplies you may need, including alkaline batteries for radios and lights, food, water, and other supplies on your checklist. Contact your spouse, children, or other family members to let them know what is happening and where you will be. Give them any instructions they will need to be safe. Tell them when you will next try to contact them, and how to contact you if necessary. Knowing that everyone is OK can let you do your job without needless worry, and, of course, the same is true for them.

Reference links:

Review:

The "emcomm activation liaisons" are several people who can be contacted by the served agency to activate the emcomm group. Notification systems can use telephone trees, commercial or Amateur paging systems, email, or simple CTCSS receiver activation. Regardless of which primary notification method your group uses, there should be several backup methods as well. Each member should know where to go, what frequencies to monitor, and what nets to check into immediately after notification.

Student activities:

1. List the strengths and weaknesses of the telephone tree as an alerting system.

2. List the strengths and weaknesses of paging as an alerting system.

3. List the strengths and weaknesses of self-activation as an alerting system.

4. Design an emcomm activation system for a seven member team. Be sure to include back up methods.

Questions:

1. When a telephone tree is activated, what should be done when a caller cannot reach one of their assigned contacts?
A. Call all those assigned to the person who cannot be reached.
B. Call the liaison to report the difficulty.
C. Ignore that person and go on to the next assigned contact.
D. Stop calling at that point to "break" the tree.

2. What is an "emcomm activation liaison" for a served agency?
A. A phone answering service employed by the agency
B. An automatic paging service employed by the agency.
C. An agency employee who arrives early to turn on the equipment.
D. A member of an emcomm group who is alerted first by the agency.

3. Regarding emcomm alerting systems, which of the following is true?
A. All systems are equally useful.
B. As an alerting system, commercial paging is clearly superior to all others.
C. As an alerting system, the telephone tree is clearly superior to all others.
D. It is best not to rely exclusively upon any single alerting system.

4. Which of the following is true of e-mail as an alerting system?
A. With e-mail, emcomm members can be reached immediately anywhere they happen to be.
B. With e-mail, high-speed Internet connections guarantee that messages will be received very quickly.
C. E-mail is best used as a back up alerting system.
D. With e-mail, the CTCSS tone assures that all members will be quickly alerted.

5. Which of the following statements is true about the NCS?
A. The NCS is so important that it should never be assigned on a temporary basis.
B. The NCS is so important that temporary assignment as NCS should be limited to only one member of the group.
C. The NCS is so important that several members should be trained to take on the duties until the assigned NCS checks in.
D. The first member to sign on to a net is always the NCS for the duration of the incident.

Learning Unit 15

Setup, Initial Operations, and Shutdown

Objectives:

Following completion of this Learning Unit, you will understand the steps necessary to set up, begin, and end operations in temporary locations, such as shelters in schools or churches, or temporary command centers at any location.

Student Preparation Required:

None.

Information:

Responding After The Activation

If you already have your assignment, confirm that monitoring and checking into the local activation net is activating it. If you do not have a standing assignment, you should check into activation net and request an assignment. It might be a "resource" logistics net if one is active, or the general "tactical" command activation net. (Since local procedures vary wide, you should get to know your group's specific plans and procedures well in advance.)

After you have gathered your equipment and are ready to respond, you may need to do several things, depending on local plans and the nature of the emergency. You may be asked to check in to a specific net to let them know you are en route, and then periodically to report your progress, particularly if travel is hazardous.

In some cases, you may be asked to proceed to a "staging" or "volunteer intake" area to wait for an assignment. This could take some time, especially if the situation is very confused. Often, the development of the response to the emergency is unclear and it will take some time to develop a cohesive and uniform response plan for that incident. You should expect the situation to be fluid as each incident is unique and to respond accordingly. Be prepared to wait patiently for a determination to be made and an assignment to be given.

In other cases, such as the immediate aftermath of a tornado or earthquake, you may be forced to make expedient arrangements as you go. Travel may be difficult or impossible, so you may need to do what you can, where you can. Nets may be established that on an ad-hoc basis using whatever means is available.

Who is in charge?

At each station, the EC or other emcomm manager should appoint one member of the emcomm group to take a leadership role as "station manager,' with full responsibility for all operations at that site. This person serves as a point person for contact, information and decisions for the team, with the incident commander and with other groups aiding in the response. This helps avoid confusion and arguments.

When you accept a position as an emcomm volunteer, you do so knowing that you will often need to follow the directions of another person. Cooperation and good teamwork are key elements that result in an efficient and effective emcomm operation. As the situation arise, you may have to step into a role of a leader to keep the operation moving forward. Those are key principles behind the success of the Incident Command System (ICS). ICS is a structured and scalable means of absorbing and organizing people from diverse agencies into a cohesive team of responders. [Expect to work with others. Expect that there are times you are the follower. Expect that other times, you may be the leader.]

Arriving at the Site

If you are assigned to a facility operated by the served agency, such as a shelter, introduce yourself to the person in charge as an "emergency communicator" assigned to serve that location. They will be busy, so get right to the point:

- Identify yourself and explain that you have been assigned to set up a communication station for that location, and by whom.
- Inform them that you would like to set up your equipment and get on the air. Ask if another communicator has already arrived. Ask if they have a preference for the station's location.
- If you are the first communicator to arrive, be prepared to suggest an appropriate location – one that can serve as both an operating and message desk, has feedline access to a suitable antenna location, access to power and telephone, and is just isolated enough from the command center to avoid disturbing each other.
- Ask if there are any hazards or considerations in the immediate area that you should be aware of, or cause you to relocate later.

If no building or other suitable shelter is available, you may need to set up your own tent, or work from your car. Choose a location that provides shelter from wind, precipitation and other hazards, and is close enough to the served agency's operations to be convenient, but not in their way.

Being a Good Guest

In many cases, you will be occupying a space that is normally used by someone else for another purpose. Respect and protect their belongings and equipment in every way possible. For instance, if you are in a school and will be using a teacher's desk, find a way to remove all the items from its surface to a safe place for the duration of operations. A cardboard box sealed and placed under the desk usually works well. Do not use their office supplies or equipment, or enter desk drawers or other storage areas without specific permission from a representative of the building's owners. Some served agencies will seal all filing cabinets, drawers, and doors to certain rooms with tamper-evident tape upon arrival to protect the host's property and records.

When installing antennas, equipment, and cables, take care not to damage anything. For instance, avoid using "duct" tape to fasten cables to walls, since its removal will usually damage the surface. If any damage is caused, make note of it in your log and report it to the appropriate person as soon as possible.

Initial Set Up And Information Gathering

In most cases, your first priority will be to set up a basic station to establish contact with the net. Pack that equipment in your vehicle last so that you can get to it first. If you arrive as a team of two or more, station setup can begin while others carry in the remaining equipment.

Set up and test the antenna for proper SWR, and then check into the net. Test to find the lowest power setting that produces reliable communication, especially if you are operating with battery or generator power, to conserve power for extended operations. High power should also be avoided whenever possible to prevent interference with other radio systems, telephones, and electronic equipment.

Once your basic station is on the air, you can begin to work on other needs:
- Check for working telephones, faxes, Internet and other means of communications
- Learning about the served agency's operations and immediate needs at that site
- Installing additional stations or support equipment
- Making a list of stations within simplex range
- Identifying possible alternative message paths
- Finding sanitary facilities
- Determining water and food sources, eating arrangements
- Reviewing overall conditions at the site, and how they will affect your operations
- Finding a place to get some occasional rest

As soon as possible, ask a member of the served agency's staff to spend a few moments to discuss the agency's operational needs. What are the most critical needs? Whom do they need to communicate with, and what sort of information will need to be transmitted? Will messages be short and tactical in nature, or consist of long lists? Will any messages be too confidential for radio? Are phones and fax still working? What will traffic needs be at different times of day? How long is the site anticipated to be open? Will there be periodic changes in key agency staff?

You may also need to provide agency staff with some basic information on how to create a message, show them how to use message forms, and instruct them on basic procedures to follow. Be sure to let them know that their communications will not be private and "secure" if sent by Amateur Radio, and discuss possible alternatives.

Ending Operations

Emcomm operations may end all at once, or be phased out over time. Several factors may affect which operations end, and when:

- Damaged communication systems are restored and returned to service
- Traffic loads are reduced and can be handled with normal systems
- Shelters and other locations are closed

How you are notified to end operations will depend on the policies of your emcomm group and served agency, and the specific situation. For instance, even though a shelter manager has been told to shut down by the served agency, your orders may normally come from a different person who may not be immediately aware of the shelter's closing. In this case, you might need to check with the appropriate emcomm manager before closing your station. Once the decision to close your station has been received and verified, be sure that the person in charge of the location is aware that you are doing so, and if necessary, why.

File and package all messages, logs, and other paperwork for travel. Return any borrowed equipment or materials. Carefully remove all antennas and equipment, taking care to package and store it correctly and safely. Avoid the temptation to toss everything into a box with the intention to "sort it out later, " unless you are under pressure to leave in a hurry. In the event you are re-deployed quickly, this will save time in the end.

Departure

Several actions may be necessary when leaving. First, be sure to leave the space you used in as good a condition as possible. Clean up any messes, remove trash, and put any furniture or equipment back where it was when you arrived. If you sealed desktop items in a box for safekeeping, simply place the box on the cleaned desk. Do not unpack the items and attempt to replace them on the desk. This will provide proof to the desk's owner that you took steps to protect their belongings, and helps keep them secure until their owner takes possession again. Do not remove tamper evident tape or similar seals placed by others unless told to do so by the appropriate person, or in accordance with the agency's policy.

Thank all those who worked with you. Even a simple verbal "thanks" goes a long way, compared to hearing not a single word. Do not forget the building's owners or staff, the served agency staff or others you worked with, and any other emcomm personnel. This is also the time for any apologies. If things did not always go well, or if any damage was caused, do your best to repair the relationship before departing. These simple efforts can go a long way toward protecting relationships between all groups and individuals involved.

The Debriefing

After each operation, your emcomm group, and perhaps even the served agency, will probably want to hold a meeting to review the effectiveness of the operation. There may be issues that occur during operations that you will want to discuss at this meeting. Events may have occurred within the served agency that involved communications you handled. If you try to rely entirely on your memory or logbooks, you will probably forget key details or even forget certain events altogether.

To prevent this from happening, keep a separate "de-briefing" diary, specifically for use during this meeting. Some entries might only refer briefly to specific times and dates in the station operating log, or they may contain details of an issue that are not appropriate in the station log. If you will be required to turn over your station logs immediately at the end of operations, your de-briefing diary will need to contain full details of all events and issues for discussion.

Such information might include:
- What was accomplished?
- Is anything still pending? Note unfinished items for follow-up.
- What worked well? Keep track of things that worked in your favor.
- What needed improvement?
- Ideas to solve known problems in the future.
- Key events
- Conflicts and resolutions

During the de-briefing, organize the session into (a) what worked well, and (b) what could be improved for the next operation. Change criticisms and judgment statements into a constructive manner by saying, "This method might have worked better if...,' rather than "This method was stupid." Also, avoid personal attacks and finger pointing. In most cases, interpersonal issues are dealt with most effectively away from the group meeting.

Reference links:
- For information about **ARRL Public Service Communications**, please see www.arrl.org/FandES/field/pscm/index.html or **The Public Service Communication Manual** at www.arrl.org/FandES/field/pscm/sec1-ch1.html.
- For specific information on **ARES**, see the **ARES Field Manual** (.pdf file) at www.arrl.org/FandES/field/aresman.pdf

Review:

The process of setting up, operating, and taking down your station should be an orderly one. A little advance planning can save considerable time. From the very first minute, work closely with served agency personnel to pick a location for your station, and learn what their operational needs are. Protect the building and its contents in every way possible. Log all events and issues for discussion in the post-event debriefing.

Student activities:

Choose and complete two activities – share the results with your mentor.

1. Suppose that you were given the assignment of coaching a new member of your emcomm group. What six rules would you teach the new member regarding behavior at a served agency?

2. Within this lesson, the following statement was made: "Pack that equipment (radio gear) in your vehicle last so that you can get to it first." This is a concept that was developed during WWII, known as "combat loading."

Consider all the gear that you might need for a three-day emcomm assignment. How might you "combat load" your gear in a vehicle?

3. Develop a checklist of actions you should take upon arrival if you were assigned to a different served agency during an emcomm event.

4. Develop a checklist of actions you should take prior to departing a served agency at the conclusion of an emcomm event.

Questions:

1. Suppose that you have been activated during an emergency and have been told to report to an agency that is different from your usual assignment. Which of the following is your best course of action upon arriving at the new agency?
A. Take charge and set up a communication center right away.
B. Check around the site and find the best place to set up a communication center.
C. Ask the receptionist about the best location for setting up a communication center.
D. Introduce yourself to the person in charge as the emergency communicator assigned to that location.

2. You have just been "activated." Which of the following would you NOT do?
A. Monitor your local ARES net for assignments.
B. Contact your EC for an assignment.
C. Head for the designated staging area.
D. Pick your favorite shelter and head right to it before anyone else does.

3. Suppose that you have been assigned to a site and the emergency ends. If the site manager asks you to close your station, what is your best course of action?
A. Do as the site manager tells you and close down your station immediately.
B. Ignore the site manager and await further instructions from higher authority.
C. Check in with the emcomm manager or NCS before closing down.
D. Have your emcomm manager or NCS speak directly with the site manager before you take any action.

4. In preparing to leave a site after an emcomm event, which of the following actions is NOT appropriate.
A. Clean up any mess, discard trash, and move furniture back to its original position.
B. Unpack all desk items that you have placed in boxes and put them back in their original locations.
C. Thank all of those who worked with you.
D. Repair any relationships that may have been strained during the event.

5. A debriefing should be scheduled after each emcomm event. What is the primary purpose of the debriefing?
A. It provides an occasion too swap "war stories."
B. It serves as a legitimate forum for complaints.
C. It serves to improve future emcomm activities.
D. It provides an occasion for resolving interpersonal issues.

Learning Unit 16

Operations & Logistics

Objectives:

This unit will help you understand and deal with some of the operating and logistical issues that arise during emergency relief and communication operations.

Student preparation required:

None

Information:

Choosing Net Frequencies

Unlike commercial and public safety radio users, Amateurs have a vast amount of radio spectrum to use in meeting the needs of an emergency. Most local and regional emcomm communication takes place on 2 meter or 70 centimeter FM, or on 40 or 80 meter SSB/CW. The choice made is based on the locations to be covered, the availability of repeaters, distance, terrain, and band conditions.

VHF and UHF FM are preferred for most local operations because of the equipment is common, portable, has a clear voice quality and the coverage is extended by repeater stations. Terrain, antenna height, and the availability of repeaters determine VHF and UHF communication range.

For larger areas or in areas without repeaters, HF SSB may be needed. Most local emcomm operation is on the 40 or 80-meter bands using Near Vertical Incidence Skywave (NVIS) propagation. For occasional long-haul communication needs and international operations, 15 or 20-meter nets may be the best option.

Many emcomm groups will have pre-selected a number of frequencies for specific purposes. The complete list of these frequencies should be in your jump kit, and pre-programmed into your radios.

Know Your Resources In Advance

Become familiar with the coverage and features of each permanent repeater and digital message system in your area, and pre-program your radios with the frequencies, offsets, and CTCSS tones. Ask your EC or AEC which repeaters are used for emergency communication in your area. Will they be available for exclusive emcomm use, or must they be shared with other users? Information to find out include:
- How does it identify itself?

- Are there any "dead spots" in critical areas? How much power is required to reach the repeater with a clear, quiet, signal from key locations?
- Does the repeater have a courtesy tone, and what does it sound like? Do the tones change depending on the repeater's mode?
- How long is the "time-out timer"?
- Is it part of a linked system of repeaters? What features does it have, and which touch-tone commands or CTCSS tones activate them?

For net frequencies that support digital communication systems, such as packet radio bulletin board messaging systems, AMTOR, PSK31 and RTTY:
- Which software do they use?
- Do the digital systems have mailboxes or digipeater functions?
- Which other nodes can they connect to? Can traffic be passed over an Internet link automatically or manually?
- How many connections can they support at once?

Network Coverage Concerns

Most emcomm managers rely on simplex operation when planning their VHF or UHF FM nets for one reason – repeaters often do not survive disasters or are overwhelmed with the amount of traffic. Repeaters that do survive and are usable are considered a bonus. Since terrain, output power, antenna gain and height limit simplex range, operation over a wide area can be a challenge. Almost any structure or hill can block signals to some degree.

To avoid last minute surprises, pre-test all known fixed locations in your area for coverage. For instance, if you are serving the Red Cross, test simplex coverage from each official shelter to the Red Cross office and the city's EOC or other key locations, and mobile coverage in the same areas. If needed, there are several ways to improve simplex range:
- Use an antenna with greater gain
- Move the antenna away from obstructions
- Use a directional antenna
- Increase antenna height
- Increase transmitter output power as a last resort.

In a fast moving situation with poor simplex coverage and no repeater, it can be helpful to place a mobile station on a hilltop or office building where they can communicate with, and relay for, any station in the net. A mobile relay station can also allow communications to follow a moving event, such a wildfire or flash flood. That station becomes, in effect, a "human repeater". Although an expedient "work-around", this is a slow and cumbersome process that can reduce net efficiency by more than half. A modern aid to this kind of operation is the "simplex repeater". This device automatically records a transmission, and immediately re-transmits it on the same frequency. Remember that FCC rules do not allow unattended operation of simplex repeaters.

A better solution is a portable duplex repeater that can be quickly deployed at a high point in the desired coverage area. The coverage of this repeater does not have to be as good as a permanent repeater – it just has to reach and hear the stations in your net. Portable repeaters have been used successfully from the back seat of a car, using a mobile antenna, and parked on a ridge or even the top floor of a parking garage. Portable masts and trailer-mounted towers have also been used successfully.

If all stations in the net have dual-band radios or scanners, a strategically located mobile radio may be operated in "cross-band repeater" mode. If you use your dual-band mobile in this manner for an extended period, use the low or medium power setting to avoid overheating and damaging your radio. Consider using a fan to further reduce the likelihood that your radio will be damaged from overheating.

For a permanent repeater to be useful in a disaster, it must have emergency power, and be in a location and of such construction that it can survive the disaster. Agreements with repeater owners should be in place to allow emergency operations to the exclusion of regular users.

Frequency and Net Resource Management

While we may have a large amount of frequency resources, in actual practice our choices are bounded to the available operators and their equipment. Net managers may occasionally need to "shift" resources to meet changing needs. In the early stages of an emergency, the tactical nets may require more operators, but in later stages, the health and welfare traffic might increase.

In addition to the main net frequency, each net should have several alternate frequencies available. These should include one or more "back up" frequencies for use in the event of interference, and one or two frequencies to be used to pass traffic "off net".

In general, each station monitors one or more frequencies. When you want to pass the traffic to another station, consider which frequency you wish to use to exchange messages. Then, find the other station's monitoring frequency and call on that frequency. If the other station is monitoring a controlled net, first ask the Net Control Station (NCS) for permission to call the other station and when permission is granted, give the other station a call. When you make contact, inform the other station of the frequency you wish to use to exchange the message, move to that frequency and pass the message.

Message Relays

When one station cannot hear another, a third station may have to "relay" the messages. Although this is a slow and cumbersome process, it is often the only way to reach certain stations. If relays must be used, move off the main net frequency to avoid tying up the channel for an extended period.

Radio Room Security

To protect your equipment and the messages you handle, and prevent unnecessary distractions, it is best to allow only the operators who are on duty to be in the room. Avoid leaving the radio room and equipment unattended and accessible. It is never a good idea to allow members of the press to be in the room without specific permission from the served agency.

Record Keeping

Most served agencies will expect you to keep records of your operations. These records will certainly include original copies of any messages sent, station logs, memos, and official correspondence. Some may even require you to keep "scratch" notes and informal logs. Depending on agency policy, you may be required to keep these records in your own possession for a time, or to turn some or all records over to the agency at the end of operations. In some agencies, your station records are permanent and important legal documents, and must be treated as such. It is important to know your served agency's policy on record keeping in advance so that you can comply from the very beginning of operations.

Your station operating logs should probably contain the following information:
- Your arrival and departure times
- Times you check in and out of specific nets
- Each message, by number, sender, addressee, and other handling stations
- Critical events – damage, power loss, injuries, earth tremors, other emergencies
- Staff changes – both emcomm and site management, if known
- Equipment problems and issues

Every individual message or note should be labeled with a time and date. In the case of scratch notes, place dates and times next to each note on a sheet, so that information can be use later to determine a course of events.

If you expect to operate from the location for more than a day or two, establish a message filing system so that you can retrieve the messages as needed. A "portable office" type file box or any other suitable container can be used to organize and file the messages. This is also an efficient way to allow another operator to pick up where you left off, even if they arrive after you leave. Effective record keeping allows them to come up to speed quickly.

Dealing With Stress and Egos

Any unusual situation can create personal stress – disasters create incredible amounts of it. Most people are not used to working under extreme stress for long periods, and do not know how to handle it. They can become disoriented, confused, unable to make good decisions or any decisions at all, lose their tempers, and behave in ways they never would any other time. Nervous breakdowns are common among those who get overwhelmed and have not learned to manage stress and stress-causing situations.

Especially in the early hours of a disaster, the tendency is to regard every situation or need as an "emergency", requiring an immediate response. You might get a barrage of requests for action. You might not have the extra seconds it requires to fully consider the options, and to prioritize your actions. The result is an overload of responsibility, which can lead to unmanageable levels of stress.

While you cannot eliminate disaster-related stress, you can certainly take steps to reduce or control it. Here are some tips to help you manage the situation to avoid creating, and deal with, excessive stress and stressful situations:

- Delegate some of your responsibilities to others. Take on those tasks only you can handle.
- Prioritize your actions –the most important and time-sensitive ones come first.
- Do not take comments personally – mentally translate "personal attacks" into "constructive criticism" and a signal that there may be an important need that is being overlooked.
- Take a few deep breaths and relax. Do this often, especially if you feel stress increasing. Gather your thoughts, and move on.
- Watch out for your own needs – food, rest, water, and medical attention.
- Do not insist on working more than your assigned shift if others can take over.
- Take a moment to think before responding to a stress-causing challenge – if needed, tell them you will be back to them in a few minutes.
- If you are losing control of a situation, bring someone else in to assist or notify a superior. Do not let a problem get out of hand before asking for help.
- Keep an eye on other team members, and help them reduce stress when possible.

Some within the emergency response community have "big egos", and still others with a need to be in full control at all times. Both personality types can be problematic anytime, but far worse under stress. Take time now to consider how you will respond to the challenges they present. If your automatic response to certain behaviors is anger, make a conscious decision to come up with a different and more positive response strategy. Depending on the official position of the "problem" person, you might:

- Do your job as best you can, and deal with it after the emergency is over
- Politely decline and state your reasons
- Refer the issue to a superior
- Choose in advance to volunteer in another capacity and avoid that person altogether

Long Term Operations

As soon as it becomes clear that the situation is not going to return to normal for a while, you and your group should make plans for extended emcomm operations. Hopefully, your emcomm group and served agency have prepared contingency plans for this, and all you will have to do is put them into action. If not, here are some potential needs to consider:

- Additional operators to allow for regular shift changes, and those who go home
- Replacement equipment, as operators leave with their own gear or it fails
- Food and water
- A suitable place to sleep or rest
- Generator fuel
- Fresh batteries
- Sanitation facilities
- Shelter
- Message handling supplies, forms
- Alternate NCS operators, backups
- Additional net resources to handle message traffic

Battery Management

If you are operating on battery power, you will eventually need to recharge your batteries. As discussed earlier, some batteries need more time to recharge than others, and this time needs to be taken into account in your planning. Deep cycle marine batteries, for instance, can require a full day or longer to fully recharge. Sealed lead-acid (SLA) batteries, also known as "gel-cells", require up to 18 hours to recharge. NiCd, LIon, and similar batteries can be recharged quite quickly, although repeated rapid charge cycles can reduce overall battery life.

If you are using slow-charging batteries, you may need to have enough on-hand to last the entire length of the operation. If your batteries can be charged quickly, some means must be provided for doing so. Some chargers can be powered from a vehicle's 12-volt system, and are a good choice for emcomm. If no local means of charging is available, your logistics team may need to shuttle batteries back and forth between your position and a location with power and chargers.

Generator and Power Safety

Take some care in the placement of generators so that they will not be a problem for others. Engine noise can make it difficult for shelter residents and volunteers to get much needed rest, and for anyone trying to do their job. Exhaust fumes should not be allowed to enter the building or nearby tents or vehicles. A position "down-wind" of any occupied location is best. Even when vehicles are not included, internal combustion engines are still the number one cause of carbon monoxide poisoning in the United States. Propane powered engines produce as much or more CO as gasoline or diesel engines.

Earth grounding of portable or vehicle-mounted AC generators is not required as long as only plug and cord connected equipment is used, and the generator meets National Electrical Code (NEC) standards listed in Article 250-6. The main exception is for generators that will be connected, even temporarily, to a building's permanent electrical system. For further details on grounding AC electrical systems, please refer to Article 250 of the NEC.

Ground Fault Interrupters (GFIs) add a further degree of safety when working with generators and portable power systems. However, GFIs will not work as intended without a good electrical ground. Be sure the ground connections in every extension cord and device are intact. Also, be sure to test any GFI device to be used with or near HF radios to be sure that the GFI will function properly while the radio is transmitting.

AC extension cords used to connect to generators or other power sources should be rated for the actual load. Most are rated for far less power than the generator can produce. Also, most extension cords are rated only for their actual length, and cannot be strung together to make a longer cord without "de-rating" the cord's capacity. For example, a typical 16ga, 50' orange "hardware store" cord is rated for 10 amps. When two are used to run 100', the rating drops to only 7 amps. Choose a single length of cord rated for the load and the entire distance you must run it. If this is not possible, you can also run two or more parallel cords to the generator in order to reduce the load on any single cord. For more information on portable power cord requirements, consult Article 400 of the NEC.

While some groups have used "Romex™" type wire for long extension cords, this is actually a violation of the National Electrical Code, and a dangerous practice. Repeated bending, rolling, and abrasion can cause the solid copper conductors and insulation to break, resulting in a fire and electrocution hazard. Use only flexible insulated extension cords that are UL rated for temporary, portable use.

Equipment – Leaving Yours Behind?

You are exhausted, and ready to head for home, but the emcomm operation is far from over. You brought along a complete station, and when you leave, the next operator is not nearly as well equipped. Should you leave your equipment behind for the next operator?

You have several options here – and they are all yours to choose from. No one can, or should, tell you to leave your equipment behind. If you feel comfortable that someone you know and trust will look after your gear, you may choose to leave some or all of it behind. If you do, be sure every piece is marked with at least your name and call sign. Do not leave behind anything the next operator does not truly need. Also, remember that even if you leave the equipment in the possession of someone you know, you still have the ultimate responsibility for its operation and safety. Emergency stations are difficult places to control and monitor. If your equipment is stolen, lost, or damaged, you should not hold anyone responsible but yourself. Conversely, if someone leaves their equipment in your care, treat and protect it better than you would your own, and be sure it is returned safely to its owner.

Accepting Specialized Assignments

In the world of modern emcomm, you may be asked to handle other assignments for the served agency that may or may not include communicating. At one time, most emcomm groups had strict policies against doing other tasks, and this is still true of some. In the days when radios were difficult to operate under field conditions and required constant attention, this was important. The other common reason given is that you have volunteered to be a communicator, not a "bed pan changer". It is true that some agency's staff will abuse the situation when they are short of help, but if both the agency and emcomm group are clear about any limits beforehand, the problem should not arise.

Today, most emcomm groups will permit their members to be cross-trained for, and perform, a variety of served-agency skills that *also include communicating*. Examples are Skywarn weather spotting, Red Cross damage assessment, and many logistics jobs. If your group still has a "communication only" policy, are you really meeting your agency's needs? Is it necessary to have a damage assessment person AND a communicator to do that job? What would happen to your agency if each driver also had to bring along a dedicated radio operator? Can one person do both jobs?

Reference links:
- For information about **ARRL Public Service Communications**, please see www.arrl.org/FandES/field/pscm/index.html or *The Public Service Communications Manual*.
- For specific information on **ARES**, see the ARRL ARES Field Resources Manual (.pdf file)

Review:

Simplex operation is preferred over repeaters because repeaters often fail in a disaster situation. Frequencies and operators are a resource that should be managed for maximum efficiency and effectiveness. Record keeping is essential to an effective emcomm operation. It allows messages to be tracked, and preserves continuity when personnel change. Demanding situations like disasters can breed disagreements, especially when strong egos and short-fused tempers are introduced. Take steps to reduce the level of stress on yourself, and do not respond in kind to an angry person. When an operation looks like it will be an extended one, begin immediately to prepare for the additional people and resources necessary to sustain the operation. Arrange to charge batteries as needed. Use generators and power distribution equipment safely. Leaving your equipment behind is a choice only you can make. Think about that well in advance to be sure other arrangements are made before you leave with all your equipment. Modern emcomm groups often accept other agency tasks beyond just communications.

Student activities: (choose two)

1. Develop a set of "rules" to help a new emcomm group member deal with stress during an emergency.

2. Develop a list of at least five possible served agency jobs that would also require your communication skills.

3. Develop five safety rules pertaining to generators and electrical lines in and near a radio room.

Share your answers with your mentor.

Questions:

1. Which of the following will NOT limit VHF simplex range?
A. Terrain.
B. Output Power.
C. Antenna Gain.
D. Digipeaters.

2. Which of the following actions will NOT improve simplex reception?
A. Increase the antenna height.
B. Switch to a non-directional antenna.
C. Increase transmitter output power.
D. Move the antenna away from obstructions.

3. Which of the following is true about a simplex repeater?
A. The FCC rules do not permit unattended operation of simplex repeaters.
B. They work best in the "cross band repeater" mode.
C. They require the use of two radios.
D. Is the same as a "human repeater."

4. Which of the following is NOT an appropriate served agency assignment for an emcomm volunteer?
A. Field damage assessment and reporting.
B. Driving a supply delivery vehicle.
C. Typing inventory lists and filing memos.
D. Gathering weather data and reporting conditions.

5. *Which of the following is a good means of dealing with stress during an emcomm event?*

A. Take every comment personally.

B. Pay no attention to other team members; let them handle their own problems.

C. To reduce personal stress, insist on working more than your own shift.

D. Prioritize your actions - the most important and time sensitive ones come first.

Learning Unit 17

Personal Safety, Survival, and Health Considerations

Objectives:

This unit will help you make informed decisions that will protect your own health and safety in a disaster environment, and that of your family as well.

Student Preparation Required:

None

Information:

Disaster relief volunteers sometimes become so involved with helping others that they forget to take care of their own families and themselves. The needs of disaster victims seem so large when compared with their own that volunteers can feel guilty even taking a moment for their own basic personal needs. However, if you are to continue to assist others, you need to keep yourself in good condition. If you do not, you risk becoming part of the problem. If your family is not safe and all their needs taken care of, worrying about them may prevent you from concentrating on your job.

Home and Family First

Before leaving on an assignment, be sure you have made all necessary arrangements for the security, safety, and general well being of your home and family. Family members, and perhaps friends or neighbors should know where you are going, when you plan to return, and a way to get a message to you in an emergency.

If you live in the disaster area or in the potential path of a storm, consider moving your family to a safe location before beginning your volunteer duties. Take whatever steps you can to protect your own property from damage or looting, and let a neighbor or even local police know where you are going, when you plan to return, and how to reach you or your family members in an emergency.

In addition to your emcomm deployment checklists, you might want to create a home and family checklist. It should cover all their needs while you are gone. Here are some ideas to get you started:

House
- Board up windows if you are in a storm's path
- Put lawn furniture and loose objects indoors if high winds are likely
- Remove valuables from the basement if flooding is possible
- Heating fuel tanks should be filled

- Drain pipes if below freezing temperatures and power loss is possible
- Shut off power and gas if practical and if structural damage is possible

Family
- Safe place to stay if needed, preferably with friends or relatives
- Reliable transportation, with fuel tank filled
- Adequate cash money for regular needs and emergencies (not ATM or credit cards)
- House, auto, life, and health insurance information to take along if evacuated
- Access to important legal documents such as wills, property deeds, etc.
- Emergency food and water supply.
- AM/FM radio and extra batteries
- Flashlight and extra batteries, bulbs
- Generator, fuel and safe operating knowledge
- Adequate supply of prescription medications on hand
- List of emergency phone numbers
- Pet supplies and arrangements (shelters will not take pets)
- List of people to call for assistance
- Maps and emergency escape routes
- A way to contact each other
- A plan for reuniting later

Should you leave at all?

There are times when your family may need you as much or more than your emcomm group. Obviously, this is a decision that only you and your family can make. If a family member is ill, your spouse is unsure of their ability to cope without you, if evacuation will be difficult, or any similar concern arises, staying with them may be a better choice. If there is ever any doubt, your decision must be to stay with your family. This is also something you should discuss, and come to an agreement with your spouse about well before any disaster, in order to avoid any last minute problems.

You First – The Mission Second

Once you are working with your emcomm group, you will need to continue to take care of yourself. If you become over-tired, ill, or weak, you cannot do your job properly. If you do not take care of personal cleanliness, you could become unpleasant to be around. Whenever possible, each station should have at least two operators on duty so that one can take a break for sleep, food and personal hygiene. If that is not possible, work out a schedule with the emcomm managers or your NCS to take periodic "off-duty" breaks.

Food

Most people need at least 2000 calories a day to function well. In a stressful situation or one with a great deal of physical activity you may need even more. Experienced emcomm managers and served agency personnel will usually be aware of this issue and take steps to see that their volunteer's needs are met. If you are at a regular shelter, at least some of your food needs will probably be taken care of. In other situations, you may be on your own, at least for a while. High calorie and high protein snacks will help keep you going, but you will also need food that is more substantial. You may need to bring along some freeze-dried camping food, a small pot, and a camp stove with fuel, or some self-heating military surplus "Meal, Ready to Eat" (MRE) packages.

Water

Safe water supplies can be difficult to find during and after many disasters. You will need at least two or three liters of water each day, just for drinking, more for other purposes. In extremely hot or cold conditions, or with increased physical activity, your needs will increase significantly. Most disaster preparedness checklists suggest at least one gallon per person, per day.

Many camping supply stores offer a range of water filters and purification tablets that can help make local water supplies safer. However, they all have limitations you should be aware of. Filters may or may not remove all potentially harmful organisms or discoloration, depending on the type. Those with smaller filter pores (.3 microns is a very tight filter) will remove more foreign matter, but will also clog more quickly. Iodine-saturated filters will kill or remove most harmful germs and bacteria, but are more expensive and impart a faint taste of iodine to the water. Most filters will remove Giardia cysts. All water filters require care in their use to avoid cross-contamination of purified water with dirty water.

Purification tablets, such as Halazone, have a limited shelf life that varies with the type, and give the water an unpleasant taste. Tablets will do nothing for particulate (dirt) or discoloration in the water. Be sure to read and understand the information that comes with any water purification device or tablet before purchasing or using it.

The FDA says you can use plain Clorox laundry bleach (no perfumes, etc). After filtering out any particulate by pouring it through several layers of dense cloth, put sixteen drops of Clorox in a gallon of water, mix well, and allow it to sit for thirty minutes. If it still smells slightly of chlorine, you can use it. If not, stir in sixteen more drops and wait another half hour. If it still does not smell of chlorine, discard the water and find a new supply. It will not taste great, nor will the chlorine bleach kill cysts like Giardia, but it may be enough.

If you have no other means, boiling for at least five minutes will kill any bacteria, but will not remove any particulate matter or discoloration. Boiling will leave water with a "flat" taste that can be improved by pouring it back and forth between two containers several times to reintroduce some oxygen.

Sleep

Try to get at least six continuous hours of sleep in every twenty-four hour period, or four continuous hours and several shorter naps. Bring fresh soft foam earplugs and a black eye mask to ensure that light and noise around you are not a problem. An appropriate sleeping bag, closed-cell foam pad or air mattress, and your own pillow will help give you the best chance of getting adequate rest. If caffeine keeps you awake, try to stop drinking coffee, tea, or other beverages containing caffeine at least four hours before going to bed. Allowing yourself to become over-tired can also make falling asleep difficult.

Personal Hygiene

If you pack only a few personal items, be sure they include toothpaste and toothbrush, a comb, and deodorant. If possible, bring a bar of soap or waterless hand cleaner, a small towel and washcloth, and a few extra shirts. Waterless shampoo is available from many camping stores. After two or three days without bathing, you can become rather unpleasant to be around – think of others and make an attempt to stay as clean and well-groomed as you can under the circumstances.

Safety in an Unsafe Situation

Many disaster assignments are in unsafe places. Natural disasters can bring flying or falling debris, high or fast moving water, fire, explosions, building collapse, disease, toxic chemicals, and a variety of other dangers. You should always be aware of your surroundings and the dangers they hold. Never place yourself in a position where you might be trapped, injured, or killed. Try to anticipate what might happen and plan ahead. Always have an escape plan ready in the event that conditions suddenly become dangerous. Do not allow yourself to become "cornered" – always have more than one escape route from buildings and hazardous areas.

Wear appropriate clothing. Depending on the weather, your gear might include a hard hat, rain gear, warm non-cotton layers, work gloves, and waterproof boots. Always bring several pairs of non-cotton socks and change them often to keep your feet clean and dry. Create seasonal clothing lists suitable for your climate and the types of disasters you might encounter. As a volunteer communicator, you will not generally be expected to enter environments that require specialized protective clothing or equipment. Do not worry about purchasing these items unless required by your served agency.

Avoid potentially dangerous areas. Industrial buildings or facilities may contain toxic chemicals, which can be released in a disaster. Dams can break, bridges can wash out, and buildings can collapse. Areas can become inaccessible due to flooding, landslides, collapsed structures, advancing fires, or storm surges. If you can avoid being in harm's way, you can also prevent yourself from becoming part of the problem rather than part of the solution.

Be prepared to help others find or rescue you should you become trapped or isolated. Carry a police or signal whistle and a chemical light stick or small flashlight in your pocket. Let others know where you are going if you must travel anywhere, even within a "safe" building. Try not to travel alone – bring a "buddy."

Shelter

In most cases, you will not need your own shelter for operating or sleeping. You may be able to stay or work in the emergency operations center, evacuation shelter, or even your own vehicle. However, in some cases a tent, camp trailer, motor home, or other suitable shelter may be necessary. Your choice will depend on your needs and resources.

Tents should be rated for high winds, and should be designed to be waterproof in heavy weather. Most inexpensive family camping tents will not survive difficult conditions. Dome tents will shed wind well, but look for published "wind survival" ratings since not all dome designs are equal. Your tent should have a full-coverage rain fly rather than a single waterproof fabric. The tent's bottom should be waterproof, extending up the sidewalls at least six inches in a "bath-tub" design, but bring an extra sheet of plastic to line the *inside* just in case. (Placing a plastic ground cloth under a tent will allow rain to quickly run under and through a leaky tent floor.) Bring extra nylon cord and long ground stakes to help secure the tent in windy conditions. If you are not an experienced foul weather camper, consider consulting a reputable local outfitter or camping club for advice on selecting and using a tent.

Medical Considerations

If you have a medical condition that could potentially interfere with your ability to do your job, it is a good idea to discuss this with your physician ahead of time. For instance, if you are a diabetic, you will need to avoid going for long periods without proper food or medication, and stress may affect your blood sugar level. Persons with heart problems may need to avoid stressful situations. Even if your doctor says you can participate safely, be sure you have an adequate supply of appropriate medications on hand, and a copy of any prescriptions. Let your emcomm manager and any work partners know of your condition so that they can take appropriate actions if something goes wrong. Keep a copy of any special medical information and emergency phone numbers in your wallet at all times.

Protect Your Eyes and Sight

If you wear eyeglasses or contact lenses, bring at least one spare pair. If you use disposable contact lenses, bring more than enough changes to avoid running out. Some contact lens wearers may want to switch to glasses to avoid having to deal with lens removal and cleaning under field conditions. If you have any doubts, consult your eye doctor ahead of time. Bringing a copy of your lens prescription along may also be a good idea, especially if you are likely to be some distance from home for a while.

Sunglasses may be a necessity in some situations. Working without them in bright sun can cause fatigue, and possibly eye damage. If you are in an area with large expanses of snow or white sand, prolonged periods of exposure can cause the retina to be burned, a very painful condition commonly known as "snow blindness." Since no painkiller will help with retinal burns, it is best to use good quality UV blocking sunglasses at all times, and avoid prolonged exposure.

If you do not normally wear eyeglasses, consider a pair of industrial safety glasses or goggles to protect your eyes from wind-blown water, dust, and debris. Keep all spare eyeglasses or safety glasses/goggles in a felt-lined hard-shell storage case to prevent scratching and breakage.

Sample Personal Survival and Comfort Needs Checklist (Modify according to your own situation)
- Suitable size backpack or duffel bag for clothing and personal gear
- Plastic storage tub for food, cooking gear
- Toilet kit – soap, comb, deodorant, shampoo, toothbrush, toothpaste
- Toilet paper in zipper-lock freezer bag
- Small towel and washcloth
- Lip balm
- Facial tissues
- Sunscreen
- Insect repellent
- Prescription medications (1 week supply)
- Copies of medication and eyeglass/contact lens prescriptions
- Spare eyeglasses or contact lenses and supplies
- Hand lotion for dry skin
- Small first aid kit
- Non-prescription medications, including painkiller, antacids, anti-diarrheal, etc.
- Extra basic clothing – shirts, socks, underwear
- Gloves, for protection or warmth
- Pocket flashlight
- Folding pocket knife
- Sleeping bag, closed-cell foam pad or air mattress, pillow
- Ear plugs (soft foam type in sealed package)
- Black eye mask
- Outer clothing for season and conditions (rain gear, parka, hat, face mask, etc)
- Hard hat
- Reflective vest, hat
- Travel alarm clock
- Chemical light sticks
- Police or signal whistle
- Dust masks
- Phone/email/address list for family, friends, neighbors, physician, pharmacy
- Emergency contact/medical information card in your wallet
- Spare car and house keys
- High energy or high protein snacks
- Food – Freeze-dried or MREs

- Coffee, tea, drink mixes
- Plate or bowl, knife, fork and spoon, insulated mug
- Camp stove, small pot, fuel and matches
- Battery or other lantern
- Water, in heavy plastic jugs
- Water purification filter or tablets
- Magnetic compass, maps
- Duct tape, parachute cord

Consider packing individual items or kits in zipper-lock freezer bags to keep the contents dry, clean, and neat.

Reference links:

FEMA Disaster Safety Information: http://www.fema.gov/library/respfact.htm
FEMA Disaster Preparedness for kids: http://www.fema.gov/kids/ready.htm
American Red Cross – Disaster Safety:
http://www.redcross.org/services/disaster/keepsafe/
Family Disaster Kit: http://www.ces.ncsu.edu/depts/fcs/disaster/disaster3.html
Food: http://www.fcs.uga.edu/pubs/current/FDNS-E-34-CS.html
Water:
http://www.bae.ncsu.edu/programs/extension/publicat/wqwm/emergwatersuppl.html
North Carolina Cooperative Extension Service – food safety & disaster recovery:
http://www.ces.ncsu.edu/depts/foodsci/agentinfo/hot/natdis.html
Institute for Home and Business Safety: http://www.ibhs.org/
Univ. of Florida – Disaster safety tips: http://www.agen.ufl.edu/~foodsaf/dh039.html
Virginia Tech – Farm preparedness:
http://www.ext.vt.edu/news/periodicals/livestock/aps-98_07/aps-937.html

Review:

As important as the mission might seem, you must first take steps to protect your own home, family, and health. Plan well ahead, and include other members of your family in your planning. Let others know where you will be and how to reach you. To avoid becoming part of the problem, bring along the items you will need to be comfortable, clean, and safe.

Student Activities:

Do all of the following, and share the results with your mentor.
1. Prepare a disaster preparedness checklist specifically for your home and family.
2. Prepare a personal-needs checklist for yourself.
3. What are two major disaster threats in your area? For each threat, list five actions you would take as a precaution to protect your home and family.

Questions:

1. Which of the following statements concerning water purification is FALSE?
A. Boiling water for a full 5 minutes will kill most harmful bacteria.
B. Boiling water to purify it can leave it with a flat taste.
C. Filters may or may not remove harmful bacteria.
D. Purification tablets will remove bacteria and particulate matter (dirt).

2. Which of the following is true about using chlorine to purify water?
A. It is best to use four to six drops of chlorine per gallon of water.
B. Adding the proper amount of chlorine to water will improve the taste.
C. Adding the proper amount of chlorine to water will kill cysts like Giardia.
D. It is best to use sixteen drops of plain chlorine per gallon of water.

3. Which of the following is true about the personal gear you bring to a long-term incident?
A. Include several pairs of warm cotton socks.
B. Lightweight summer clothing is all you will ever need.
C. Keep spare eyeglasses or safety glasses/goggles in a hard-shell, felt-lined storage case.
D. As a volunteer communicator, you will need to bring specialized protective clothing.

4. Many disaster assignments are in unsafe places. Which of the following is true about such locations?
A. Always plan an escape route from buildings and hazardous areas.
B. Always plan more than one escape route from buildings and hazardous areas.
C. The only dangers that you need be concerned with in any location are fire, flood, and falling debris.
D. Dams, bridges and buildings can generally be thought of as "safe zones."

5. Which of the following statements about safety and survival is true?
A. The mission takes priority over everything else.
B. A person requires at least four gallons of water per day just for drinking.
C. If caffeine keeps you awake, stop drinking caffeinated beverages at least ten minutes before going to bed.
D. Your personal safety and well-being are a higher priority than the mission.

6. Which of the following best defines an MRE package?
A. Mainly Radio Equipment.
B. Mostly Random Equipment.
C. Meals, Ready to Eat.
D. Meals, Rarely Eaten.

Learning Unit 18

Modes, Methods, and Applications

Objective:

This lesson will help you chose the correct operating mode for each situation in an emcomm environment.

Student preparation required:

You should be generally familiar with phone (voice), CW, packet, and other digital modes.

Information:

Your purpose as emergency communicators is to provide accurate and rapid transfer of information from one place to another. To do that job well, you must understand the strengths and weaknesses of each mode of communication. In addition, you must be thoroughly familiar with the needs and priorities of the agencies you are serving. Some messages must be delivered quickly, and others are less urgent. Some are detailed, and some are simple. Sometimes you should not even use radio.

Some Concepts to Consider

Communication modes fall into several categories:
- Point to point – Telephone, fax, some digital radio modes
- Multi-point – Voice and CW radio, some digital modes
- High precision – Fax, e-mail, digital modes
- Low precision – Voice, CW, telephone
- High priority – Voice, telephone
- Low priority – Fax, e-mail, digital modes, CW

Messages fall into similar categories:
- Point to point – Messages intended for one party
- Point to multi-point – Messages intended for a group
- Multi-point to point – Messages from members of a group directed to one station
- High precision – Lists of items, medical or technical terminology, specialized or detailed information
- Low precision – Traffic reports, damage estimates, simple situation reports
- High priority – Fast delivery is critical
- Low priority – Messages can be delivered in a more relaxed time frame

Each type of message should be sent using the most appropriate mode, taking into consideration the message's contents, and its destination(s).

An example might serve to illustrate these concepts. A localized flash flood hit a north Florida county a few years ago, prompting the evacuation of a low-lying neighborhood. The Red Cross opened a shelter in a church several miles away from the affected area. ARES was mobilized to provide communication support.

In spite of the weather, the shelter still had electricity and phone service. When the county Emergency Coordinator (EC) stopped by the site, the ARES operator on duty was using his battery-operated 2-meter hand-held radio and the wide-area repeater to talk to Red Cross HQ across town. The ham was reading a three-page list of names and addresses of evacuees who had checked into the shelter. To ensure proper transcription, he was spelling each name phonetically, pausing after each name to see if the headquarters station needed fills. Needless to say, this was a time-consuming process. The operator had been reading for almost 15 minutes and was still on the second page of the list.

Less than 10 feet away from his operating position sat a fax machine. The EC turned on the machine, dialed the Red Cross fax number, and fed in the remaining page of the list. The ham on duty had used over 15 minutes of airtime and precious battery capacity to read two pages. The third page was faxed in less than 20 seconds.

Neither the operator at the shelter nor the one at headquarters had considered using the telephone or fax machine, even though these communication options were available and functioning. In all fairness to the hams in this situation, their training and practice had led them to concentrate on 2-meter voice to the exclusion of other modes of communication. So, instead of an efficient, point-to-point communication channel (telephone line), they had used a busy multi-point channel (the wide-area repeater). Instead of using a mode that generated automatic hard copy, they used one that required handwritten transcription. Instead of a high-precision transfer (fax), they had used a low-precision one (voice) requiring spelling and phonetics. The situation was especially poignant because the repeater had been needed at the time for a different type of communication – the transfer of mobile operator's reports, which could not be done over the telephone. Further, it was later discovered that the "broadcast" of evacuee's names and addresses over non-secure communication channels was a violation of Red Cross policy.

Of course, telephones and fax machines will not be available in every emergency. Sometimes only one mode will be available, especially when the emergency is totally unanticipated, utility service is interrupted over a wide area and the communicators are caught unprepared. But, with proper planning you can increase the likelihood that more than one option will be available. After all, we go to great lengths to make sure that 2 meter radios are readily available, so why not other communication options as well?

Tactical Messages:

Tactical messages are usually low-precision and time-critical, and can be passed most efficiently using voice. Depending on the nature of the message, it may take the form of formal written traffic, or at the other extreme, it may mean that the microphone is handed to a person from the served agency. This is frequently the quickest way to get the job done.

Lists and Detailed Messages:

Some messages contain long lists of supplies, or details where accuracy is important. Voice transmission can introduce errors, and long messages can waste valuable net resources. The various digital modes (including land-line fax and email) offer the best means of handling these messages, since they are both fast and accurate. Digital messages also have the benefit of repeatable accuracy. When a message is passed through several stations, it remains unchanged since no operator intervention occurs.

Sensitive Information:

Some messages contain information that should be kept private. Reporters and the general public commonly use scanning receivers to monitor public safety and Amateur Radio communications. Names and addresses of evacuees should never be transmitted over voice channels, since thieves with scanners can use this information to loot unattended homes. Learn in advance your served agency's privacy policy regarding certain types of information.

Some groups have switched to digital modes, such as packet, in an attempt to offer more privacy. Although digital transmissions require more than a simple scanner to intercept, they cannot be relied upon for absolute privacy. The equipment needed to receive most digital modes is available, and is even built into some newer receivers. Anyone wishing to monitor digital transmissions can certainly do so. Discuss this issue with your served agency before using any Amateur Radio mode to handle sensitive messages.

Remember - any means of assuring meaningful message security on Amateur Radio would be in violation of the Part 97 prohibition against the use of codes and ciphers. If absolute privacy is required, the message should not be transmitted by Amateur Radio. In some cases, the most appropriate method might be hand delivery by a radio-dispatched courier.

Digital Modes

Traffic nets handling large volumes of written or high precision traffic should consider using one of the digital modes. Digital modes can be used to transmit long lists such as health and welfare traffic, and logistics messages involving lists of people or supplies. Some digital modes provide virtually error-free transmission and relays can be accomplished by retransmitting the received digital message without having to retype it. Packet systems can provide automatic relays.

Digital modes that do not provide automatic error correction should only be used when clean and interference-free signals can be guaranteed. These modes include RTTY, AMTOR mode A, and PSK31 in BPSK mode.

HF:

The best digital modes for HF operation are packet, AMTOR mode B, and PSK31 in QPSK mode. In general, antenna and radio considerations are similar to voice or CW operation, although certain digital signals require less power than voice modes to achieve the same effect.

VHF/UHF:

The TNC2 (Terminal Node Controller, Version 2) FM packet is the most common mode used on VHF and UHF frequencies. The antenna and coverage considerations are the same as for FM voice.

Packet:

Packet communication is error-free in point to point "automated repeat request" (ARQ) or "forward error correction"(FEC) broadcast modes. The most effective way to send messages via packet radio is to use a "bulletin board." The sending station "posts" his messages on the bulletin board, and other stations can then retrieve their messages at will. Urgent messages can also be sent directly to the receiving station if needed.

Bulletin-board stations are also useful when a number of stations are sending messages to a single point, such as a command post, weather service office, or emergency operations center. Similarly, bulletin boards can be useful in handling outgoing traffic. Stations with traffic can post messages to the bulletin board. The traffic handlers can periodically pick up the traffic and send it to the outbound NTS nets.

If your group is using FM packet, ask if transmissions are simplex point to point, or if nodes, digipeaters, or bulletin-board forwarding systems are being used. You will need to know which frequencies and modes are used and for what purpose, what their callsigns or aliases are, and how various parts of the system interconnect.

A consideration is that multipath propagation may distort digital signals enough to cause failure when a voice might still be understandable. The solution is the same as in voice mode – move the antenna a few inches or feet until you get a clear signal.

AMTOR Mode B:

AMTOR mode B (also known as "FEC" mode) is an advanced teletype mode with forward error correction, making it ideal for high precision messages over long distances.

PSK31:

The ability of PSK31 to be usable in very poor conditions makes it ideal for HF emergency communication. In addition, the efficiency resulting from the very narrow bandwidth of the PSK31 signal means that even a low power transmitter will work quite well. There are two PSK31 modes: BPSK, which has no error correction, and QPSK, which has forward error-correction. BPSK should be used unless the received copy is poor, since QPSK is 3dB less efficient and requires more careful tuning. Under all but the worst conditions, BPSK will provide perfect transmissions.

Packet Teleprinting over Radio (PACTOR):

This is a combination of packet and AMTOR. It is designed for HF use only, and combines the best features of both. PACTOR uses FEC and ARQ modes, and a standard keyboard. PACTOR is quite robust (more so than AMTOR and RTTY), but can be slowed by poor band conditions.

TCP/IP Packet:

TCP/IP Internet protocols and network services are useable on packet radio. TCP/IP systems have advantages over conventional packet protocols that could be important in Amateur emcomm operations. One IP system is JNOS, which has extensions written by Johannes Reinalda, WG7J, to the original NOS (Network Operating System) written by Phil Karn, KA9Q.

- JNOS is a TCP/IP oriented e-mail system. If you're familiar with Internet e-mail, you're familiar with typing e-mail into JNOS.
- It sends e-mail via SMTP mail protocol and can interface to Internet. A JNOS station can relay packet radio messages to the Internet and vice versa, unattended.
- It will print incoming messages automatically onto a printer, unattended. If the printer is a cut-sheet printer such as an inkjet or laser printer, individual messages will automatically appear on separate sheets.
- The operator can open up to eight windows for multiple sessions for messaging. It has a ninth window for command mode for controlling the system, and a tenth window for debugging.
- It can multi-task efficiently on a 386 computer with 1megabyte of memory. In a minimal configuration, it can run on a PC/XT (640KB 8086) as an end-node station.
- It supports multiple communications ports and multiple radio/TNC combinations.
- It is shareware, and is available on the internet.

APRS:

While not a message-handling mode, APRS is a digital information mode with applications in emcomm. Originally called "Automatic Position Reporting System," this mode is now sometimes called "Automatic Packet Reporting System," owing to new applications of the technology. The newest application of APRS is the automated reporting of data from digital weather stations. The original application for APRS, developed byBob Bruninga WB4APR, is to track a station's location. A GPS receiver is connected to a computer, and its position information is transmitted to other stations using APRS packet software, displaying the location of the sending station on a map. APRS also has a messaging mode similar to Internet "Instant Messaging" where quick one-line messages can be exchanged.

APRS has two obvious applications for emcomm. First, the locations of various emergency vehicles can be tracked visually in real time in an automated and unattended fashion. Second, weather and other environmental data can be reported automatically in near real-time. Both applications can both speed data acquisition and reduce the work load on critical emergency nets.

Related considerations:

Become familiar with, and practice using, any digital mode or system well in advance of an emergency. Most are complex enough that some experience is required to use them efficiently and effectively.

Digital communications can be enhanced by composing the message off-line in a text editor. With a little ingenuity, "fill in the blank" forms can be created in most word processors to reduce the amount of typing required and help standardize message formats. For packet communication, consider an emcomm-specific program like ARESPACK (see *Reference Links* below).

The high duty-cycle of many digital modes requires a rugged radio and power supply with adequate cooling. Test your equipment under field conditions for an extended period of time to identify any possible problems.

Amateur Television (ATV)

There are two forms of ATV – slow-scan and fast-scan. Fast-scan ATV is live, full motion TV similar to what you see on commercial TV, but usually at reduced quality. Slow-scan ATV uses a voice-grade channel to send a still picture line by line. It can take more than a minute for a color picture to be transmitted.
ATV has a number of emcomm applications, but all involve letting emergency managers see what is going on in the field without ever leaving their offices. ATV crews ususaly take a passive "observer" approach, and avoid interaction with bystanders to ensure that a situation is accurately represented. No emcomm ATV transmission should ever be "staged" for the camera.

Reference Links:

PSK31--Has RTTY's Replacement Arrived? By Steve Ford, WB8IMY
Surfin': Make a Packet Racket with a Sound Card By Stan Horzepa, WA1LOU

Getting Started in Digital Communications - RTTY, Packet, Amtor, PSK31
ARESPACK software (free download)

Review:

Choosing the correct mode and frequency for each type of message will make your nets more efficient and improve service to your agency. Voice modes are low precision, multi-point modes, and many digital modes are high precision point to point modes. Sometimes, Amateur Radio is not the best way to send a message. Confidential messages are best sent via telephone, fax or courier.

Student Activities:

Choose and complete two, and share the results with your mentor.

1. Consider your own personal radio resources. Of the modes mentioned within this lesson, which would you consider acquiring for your own use? Why? Which would you not consider acquiring? Why not?

2. Select three of the digital modes. Identify the positive and negative aspects of using each of the three in an emcomm situation.

3. Based on the considerations you have identified above, develop a simple communication equipment plan for a small emcomm unit based in a small community. Within your plan, be sure to identify the equipment and modes you would employ.

4. How would the plan you developed above be different if your emcomm group were quite large and located in a large community?

Questions:

1. Which of the following best describes your purpose as an emergency communicator?
A. To operate the radio.
B. To coordinate communications for the EOC.
C. To provide accurate and rapid transfer of information from one place to another.
D. To provide internal communication support to one (and only one) responding agency.

2. Which of the following best describes tactical messages?
A. They are high precision and time critical
B. They are low precision and time critical
C. They are point-to-point and NOT time critical
D. They are point-to-multipoint and low precision.

3. Long lists and detailed messages are best handled by which of the following modes?

A. Voice or CW

B. Fax or digital

C. CW or digital

D. Phone or fax

4. During an emergency, you are using voice transmissions to pass messages. Which of the following "guidelines" should govern your action if you were asked to transmit the names and addresses of victims?

A. Transmit the information exactly as presented to you.

B. Use a pre-established code to transmit the information.

C. If absolute privacy is required, do not transmit the information by Amateur Radio.

D. Switch to a digital mode and be assured of complete privacy.

5. Which of the following PSK31 modes has an error correction feature?

A. BPSK

B. QPSK

C. RPSK

D. SPSK

Alternate Communication Systems and Methods

Objective:

The emcomm volunteer should know the pros and cons of using alternate communication systems. This unit discusses a variety of communication options that do not depend on Amateur Radio, and some circumstances where they might be used.

Student preparation required:

Read the FCC rules on emergency communications before beginning this lesson.

Information:

There are times when a means of communication other than Amateur Radio might be appropriate. It is important to remember that your job is to communicate – regardless of the medium. Here are some possible situations:

- Communication with non-ham volunteers or emergency management personnel.
- Transmission of sensitive or lengthy information.
- Communication with the public.
- Amateur Radio equipment has failed or is not available.
- Interference is blocking use of Amateur Radio frequencies.

Legal Considerations

Licenses:

Some radio services require licenses, and others do not. However, in a true emergency as defined by the FCC, this may not be a problem. FCC rules gives anyone special permission to use "any means necessary" to communicate in order to protect life and property – *but only when no other normal means of communication is possible.* Please do not assume that this means you can just modify your radio and call for help on the local police frequency the next time you see a car crash on the highway. Law enforcement agencies are not bound by the FCC's rules. Hams who have called for "help" on police frequencies have been convicted of "interfering with a police agency" under state and local laws, even though the FCC had taken no enforcement action. In one case, the judge ruled that by modifying his radio in advance, the Amateur had committed "pre-meditated" interference, a serious charge. If you are in a position to save someone's life or property, be sure you are ready to defend your actions - and possibly lose - before pressing the mic button.

Other services, such as GMRS, require a license that is relatively easy to obtain. If your group is planning to use licensed radios, obtain your license well before any emergency and keep it current. If you own a radio, but no license, a judge could claim pre-meditation if you use it and disturb licensed users.

Using Modified Ham Radios:

While it is easy to modify many VHF and UHF Amateur radios for operation in nearby public service and business bands, it is not legal to do so. Radios used in those bands must be "Type Accepted" by the FCC for the purpose, and Amateur radios are not. If you plan to use other radio frequencies discussed in this unit, it is better to purchase the proper radio. However, if the need arises and your ham radio is all you have, the FCC will probably not prosecute you for using it - if the use falls within their strict rules for emergencies.

The Other Radio Services:

In most of the radio services listed below only voice communication is permitted. Packet and other forms of data or image transmission are illegal.

General Mobile Radio Service (GMRS):

Once known as "Class A CB, GMRS is a high power (50 watt), personal-use UHF FM radio service in which users can also license repeater stations. Each station license covers only the licensee and their immediate family, but stations of different licensees are permitted to talk to one another. 462.675 MHz is designated by the FCC as an emergency and traveler's information channel, and is monitored by REACT in many cities. Seven GMRS channels are shared with the Family Radio Service, but communication between GMRS licensees and FRS users is not permitted except in an emergency. Previously, businesses could license GMRS systems to communicate with employees. This use of GMRS is grandfathered for pre-existing licensees only.

Family Radio Service (FRS):

The Family Radio Service uses inexpensive, half-watt, UHF FM radios on 14 channels. Range can be up to two miles, but mountaintop transmissions have been heard at much greater distances. These radios are becoming quite popular with the public, and could be a good means of communication with stranded or isolated persons a short distance away. REACT recommends the use of FRS channel 1 for emergency and calling use, but the FCC has declined to make this official. Voice scrambling is permitted on FRS, and is available in a few models. This might make it useful for short-range transmission of sensitive information.

Citizen's Band (CB):

27 MHz AM CB radio is familiar to almost everyone. SSB operation is also allowed, but is less common due to the higher cost of equipment. Many of the general public still have CB radios in their vehicles, especially truckers. Since disaster relief supplies often arrive by truck, being able to communicate with and direct an incoming truck on channel 19 could be quite useful. In addition, the longer range (3-5 miles) of CB makes it useful for receiving calls for assistance on emergency channel 9 from more distant stranded or isolated persons.

Multiple Use Radio Service (MURS):

This is a relatively new radio service, intended primarily for business users, but it can be used for any legal purpose under current rules. There are five MURS channels in the VHF business band. No license is required, and transmitters are limited to two watts output. This service is perfect for establishing short-range communication with non-licensed personnel at an incident scene, command post, or within an EOC.

Public Safety Radio:

Despite the stern warning at the beginning of this lesson, there are instances where the use of police and fire radio frequencies is possible. The agency itself might allow and train you for such use, or an individual officer may ask you to use his radio to call for help when he cannot. Keep your transmissions short and to the point. Do not tie up the channel with long explanations, and cease transmitting if they tell you to.

Cellular and PCS Phones:

In a widespread disaster situation, these phone systems can quickly become overloaded. In smaller emergencies, they may still be usable. If a message is too sensitive to send via any two-way radio, try your cell phone. Cellular and PCS phone transmissions, especially digital, are considerably more secured. In addition, it is possible to send data or fax transmissions over the cellular network at slow speeds.

Non-Radio Communication

Landlines:

Do not forget the most obvious means of communication. If they are still functioning, use the telephone and fax whenever the message might be too sensitive for radio. Fax is also useful for sending long lists, and where accuracy is critical. Do not tie up a radio frequency sending a long list of supplies if a fax is available.

Couriers:

Since before the time of early Greek civilization, runners have carried messages from place to place. When we are asked to deliver a message with contents that are sensitive or very lengthy, and fax and phone lines are out of service, hand delivery might be the best choice. Acting as a courier does not eliminate the use of radio, since couriers need to be dispatched from place to place. Courier service is actually an excellent marriage of old and new technologies.

Reference links:

For more information on any of the elements presented, please consult the following links:

- Multiple Use Radio Service (MURS) rules http://www.provide.net/~prsg/murshome.htm
- Family Radio Service rules http://www.provide.net/~prsg/frs-home.htm
- General Mobile Radio Service (GMRS) rules http://www.provide.net/~prsg/part95ae.htm
- Citizen's Band (CB) rules www.reactintl.org/rules-cb.htm
- For a detailed discussion of the FCC Rules on Amateur Radio emergency communication, please see the ARRL *FCC Rule Book*, Chapter 5.

Review:

Amateur Radio may not always be the best or only means of communicating. It is important to remember that our job is to get the message through, regardless of the means. Plan to have other systems licensed and in place beforehand when possible, but improvise when necessary.

Student activity:

Choose and complete two activities. Share the results with your mentor.

1. Suggest some uses for alternate communication systems beyond those discussed here.

2. List the advantages and disadvantages for emcomm work of the following modes:
A. GMRS
B. FRS
C. CB
D. MURS

3. List the advantages and disadvantages for emcomm work of the following modes:
A. Cellular phones
B. Landlines
C. Couriers

Questions:

1. The FCC has established a rule covering Amateur Radio operators in emergencies. Which of the following statements best reflects that rule?

A. In an emergency, you may use any means possible to get a message through.

B. In an emergency, (as defined by the FCC) you may use any means necessary to get a message through.

C. In an emergency, (as defined by the FCC) an Amateur Radio Operator can use any means possible to pass a message to protect life and property.

D. In an emergency, (as defined by the FCC), you may use any means possible to pass a message to protect life and property, but only when NO other normal means of communication is possible.

2. Which of the following pairs represents a LEGAL combination?

A. General Mobile Radio Service and Packet transmissions

B. Family Radio Service and Digital transmissions

C. Multiple Use Radio Service and Voice transmissions

D. Citizen's Band and PSK31

3. Which of the following pairs represents an INCORRECT combination?

A. General Mobile Radio Service and 10 watts

B. Family Radio Service and one-half watt

C. Multiple Use Radio Service and two watts

D. General Mobile Radio Service and 50 watts

4. Which of the following is NOT true of cell phones?

A. Cell phones are more private than two-way radio.

B. It is possible to send fax or slow speed data over a cellular telephone network.

C. It is possible to send data over a cell phone network at high speeds.

D. In a widespread disaster, cell phone networks may become overloaded.

5. Which of the following is NOT a good reason for using a courier?

A. Couriers are useful for delivering messages that contain sensitive information.

B. Couriers are useful for delivering messages when phone lines are out of service.

C. Couriers are useful for delivering messages when doing so will prevent other, critical modes of communication from becoming overloaded.

D. Couriers are useful for delivering messages when an instant reply is required.

Learning Unit 20

Other Learning Opportunities

Objective:

This unit offers ways to develop and perfect the skills you have learned in this course.

Student Preparation Required:

Completion of all previous Learning Units.

Information:

Someone once asked a famous violinist how to get to Carnegie Hall in New York City. His answer was "practice, practice, practice."

So it is with emergency communication skills. If you want your performance in the next big disaster to be flawless, practice is essential. Fortunately, there are plenty of opportunities to do so if you take the time to seek them out.

Regularly Scheduled Nets

Many local ARES and RACES groups hold regularly scheduled training nets. Well-designed nets will vary the format and goals frequently in order to keep them interesting. One month may be devoted to learning about the county's new damage report form, and another with moving welfare messages to and from the National Traffic System (NTS).

If ARES and RACES do not hold regular nets, consider joining an NTS net. Many areas have VHF traffic net, and if you have HF capability you can participate in regional and cross-country nets as you develop your skills.

Local Classroom and On-Air Training Sessions:

Your emcomm organization and/or served agency may offer a variety of educational opportunities. All three ARRL ARECC courses are offered in a classroom version. Local agencies may offer job specific training, such as the American Red Cross' *Introduction to Disasters* and *Disaster Damage Assessment* courses. Smaller training sessions may deal with the use of certain forms or procedures. In addition to regular nets, special on-air training sessions may be held on a repeater or simplex frequency as an alternative to classroom sessions when the subject is simple or utilizes a net environment.

Public Service Events

As you learned in Learning Unit 10, some of the best practice for tactical disaster communication is your local "athon." It does not matter if it is a bike-athon, walk-athon or crawl-athon, but the larger the event, the better the experience. A large, fast moving event closely simulates the conditions experienced in disaster communication situations. Even a slower event will allow you to practice tactical net operating skills or experiment with various modes.

Learning Resources on the Internet

We strongly recommend downloading and printing copies of the *ARES Handbook*, *ARRL Public Service Manual*, and *ARES field Resources Manual*. Put them in a three ring binder and make them part of your jump kit for easy reference at home or in the field.

- ARRL Section Manager List www.arrl.org/field/org/smlist.html
- ARRL Net Directory www.arrl.org/FandES/field/nets/
- ARRL Public Service Manual www.arrl.org/FandES/field/pscm/
- FEMA Institute www.fema.gov/emi/ishome.htm
- ARES Manual (.pdf file) www.arrl.org/FandES/field/aresman.pdf
- FCC Rules and Regulations www.arrl.org/FandES/field/regulations/rules-regs.html
- National SKYWARN http://www.SKYWARN.org/
- NWS Storm Watch http://www.noaa.gov/stormwatch/
- Ham Radio at the NWS Hurricane Center http://www.fiu.edu/orgs/w4ehw/
- NWS Doppler Radar Sites http://weather.noaa.gov/radar/national.html
- NWS Storm Prediction Center, Norman, Oklahoma http://www.spc.noaa.gov/

The Real World

- Alabama Tornados, 2000
  http://www.abc3340.com/weather/Dec2000Tornadoes.html
  http://www.alert-alabama.org/audio.html
  http://www.kr4tz.org/al-arrl/article.php3?ID=20001218.001

Books

- The *ARES Field Resources Manual* (ARRL) is a handy and rugged spiral bound field guide packed with essential emcomm information. It should be in the ready kit of every emcomm volunteer.
- The *ARRL Operating Manual* covers all the basics of Amateur Radio operation – and more.
- The *ARRL FCC Rules Handbook* offers a clear and understandable explanation of the FCC Rules and Regulations for Amateur Radio. Chapter 5 deals with emergency communication issues.
- *Your Packet Companion* by Steve Ford (ARRL) is the perfect book for packet beginners.
- *Practical Packet Radio* by Stan Horzepa (ARRL) covers the basics and delves into BBS operation, packet cluster, satellites, and more.
- *Packet: Speed, More Speed, and Applications* (ARRL) is for the advanced packet user. Topics include high-speed networks, pacsats, meteor scatter, and APRS. This book is not for beginners.

- *ARRL's HF Digital Handbook, 2nd Edition*, covers PSK31, MFSK16 and other popular digital modes.
- *APRS Tracks, Maps and Mobile –A Guide to the Automatic Packet Reporting System.* (ARRL)
- *NOSintro: TCP/IP Over Packet Radio* is an introduction to using the KA9Q Network Operating System in a packet environment. NOS has a variety of uses and implications for emcomm.
- *Transmitter Hunting: Radio Direction Simplified* by Joseph Moell, K0OV, and Thomas Curlee, WB6UZZ (ARRL) is the "bible" of radio direction finding. Topics include search and rescue operations and hunting for downed aircraft.
- *The Interference Handbook* by William Nelson WA6FQG will help you locate and resolve all sorts of radio interference.
- *The ARRL Antenna Book, Volume 4* covers portable and emergency antennas for 40 and 80 meters.
- *Weather Satellite Handbook* by Ralph Taggart WB8DQT (ARRL) offers information on how to receive and decode data directly from various weather satellites.
- *The ARRL Repeater Directory* lists all VHF and UHF repeaters in the USA, Canada and many other countries. This directory is updated annually.
- *The North American Repeater Atlas* (ARRL) has maps showing all repeaters in North America. This is a great resource for ARESMAT members traveling to unfamiliar areas.
- *Your Mobile Companion* by Ralph Burch WF4N, (ARRL) is a practical guide to installing and operating a HF mobile station.

Software

Tucson Amateur Packet Radio (TAPR) has a variety of packet software available. http://www.tapr.org/

ARESPACK is a DOS based packet messaging software that offers uniform message formats, message creation templates, and more. It is available from a variety of sites as a free download. No support or upgrades are offered or planned by the author. http://www.users.erols.com/sagers/arespack30.exe

ARESDATA is a packet-based database for tracking shelter residents and other database tasks. It is available from a variety of sites as a free download. http://www.users.erols.com/sagers/aresdata.zip

Virginia Digital Emergency Network (VDEN) http://www.erols.com/sagers

ARECC Levels II and III

ARECC Level II is designed for those who wish to further develop net management skills. The course is designed to prepare you for the jobs of NCS and Net Manager.

ARECC Level III is designed for emergency communication managers at all levels. If you are, or plan to be, an AEC, EC, DEC, or SEC, this is the course for you. Level III is also recommended for Net Managers.

Review:

Emcomm education is an ongoing process. To be an asset to your emcomm organization and its served agencies, you should take advantage of every possible learning opportunity.

Student activities:

1.Choose the next step you will take to either become involved with a local emcomm group, and/or the next step in your emcomm education. Share your choices with your mentor.

2. Suppose that you were placed in charge of training a new group of emcomm team members. To what five topics would you give the highest priority?

Questions:

1. Which of the following was NOT recommended as a means of practicing actual emcomm skills?
A. Regularly scheduled nets
B. On-air training sessions
C. Discussion groups and lectures
D. Public service events

2. What is the purpose of the next course in this series (ARECC Level II)?
A. To reinforce the skills and knowledge presented in ARECC Level I.
B. To provide training for prospective Emergency Operation Center Managers.
C. To prepare individuals for the jobs of NCS and Net Manager.
D. To prepare individuals for the jobs of DEC or SEC.

3. What is the purpose of the third course in this series (ARECC Level III)?
A. To reinforce the skills and knowledge presented in ARECC Level II.
B. To provide training for prospective Emergency Operation Center Managers.
C. To prepare individuals for the jobs of NCS and Net Manager.
D. To prepare individuals for management level emcomm positions.

Appendix A

Learning Unit 1	Learning Unit 2	Learning Unit 3	Learning Unit 4
1. D	1. C	1. B	1. D
2. A	2. B	2. C	2. D
3. A	3. D	3. C	3. A
4. B	4. C	4. C	4. C
5. C	5. C	5. D	5. C

Learning Unit 5	Learning Unit 6	Learning Unit 7	Learning Unit 8
1. A	1. B	1. C	1. B
2. B	2. A	2. A	2. D
3. A	3. C	3. C	3. C
4. D	4. C	4. D	4. C
5. C	5. D	5. C	5. D
	6. B		

Learning Unit 9	Learning Unit 10	Learning Unit 11	Learning Unit 12
1. C	1. D	1. B	1. A
2. D	2. A	2. A	2. D
3. D	3. B	3. B	3. A
4. A	4. D	4. C	4. D
5. C	5. D	5. B	5. B
		6. D	

Learning Unit 13	Learning Unit 14	Learning Unit 15	Learning Unit 16
1. D	1. A	1. D	1. D
2. C	2. D	2. D	2. B
3. D	3. D	3. C	3. A
4. B	4. C	4. B	4. C
5. D	5. C	5. C	5. D

Learning Unit 17	Learning Unit 18	Learning Unit 19	Learning Unit 20
1. D	1. C	1. D	1. C
2. D	2. B	2. C	2. C
3. C	3. B	3. A	3. D
4. B	4. C	4. C	
5. D	5. B	5. D	
6. C			

Appendix B

Learning Unit 1 Activities: List **three** ways in which Emergency Communications are **similar** to Non-emergency Communications. List **six** ways in which Emergency Communications **differ** from Non-emergency Communications. In an emergency situation, a served agency asks you to forward an urgent message. Which one of the following methods would you NOT employ? In one or two sentences, tell why you selected your answer.

a. CB radio

b. Family radio

c. Informal, conversational grapevine

d. The served agency's own radio system.

Learning Unit 2 Activities: 1. Locate the ARRL website. Conduct a search for the Statement of Understanding (SOU) between The American Red Cross and ARRL. Based on the SOU, what three forms of assistance may the Red Cross request of ARRL ARES and NTS?

Second, If you were asked to develop a Statementemo of Understanding (SOU) between your local emcomm group and a local served agency, what general topics would you include?

Appendix B (continued)

Learning Unit 3 Activities: The following activities are designed to familiarize you with the ARES information provided on the ARRL website. Follow the link below and read the ARES information provided:

1. Go the ARRL website (http://www.arrl.org/). Locate the SOU between ARRL and the American National Red Cross. Answer the following questions:
   A. According to the SOU, how is a "disaster" defined?

2. Go to the ARRL web site (http://www.arrl.org/FandES/field/pscm/foreword.html) section entitled "Public Services Communications Manual." Find the answers to the following questions:
   A. Is owning emergency-powered equipment a requirement for joining ARES?
   B. Who can authorize RACES operation?
   C. If the President were to invoke his War Emergency Powers, would there be any restrictions on Amateur Radio operation? If so, how would the two-meter band be affected?
   D. What are the two primary components of ARRL's public service field organization?

Learning Unit 4 Activities: Using the links provided, answer the following questions:
   A. What is APCO Project 39? What might Project 39 mean for emcomm operations?
   B. What do Sections 97.403 and 97.405 of FCC Rules Part 97 state about Amateur communications during emergencies?
   C. Which courses offered by IMSA pertain to radio operations? To what extent do these courses pertain to emcomm operations?

Appendix B (continued)

Learning Unit 5 Activities: Using what you have learned, edit the following exchange to make it clear and concise.

"KA1XYZ at Ramapo Base, this is Bob, K2ABC at Weston EOC calling."

"K2ABC, this is KA1XYZ. Hi, Bob. This is Ramapo Base, Harry at the mic. Go ahead. K2ABC from KA1XYZ."

"KA1XYZ, this is K2ABC returning. Hi, Harry. I have a message for you. By the way, remember to call me later about the get-together the club is having next month. Are you ready to copy the message?" KA1XYZ, this is K2ABC, over to you Harry."

Second, based upon what you have read in this lesson, list five errors to avoid when communicating during an emergency.

Learning Unit 6 Activities: Describe the best use of the following nets:
A. Open nets
B. Emergency nets
C. Tactical nets
D. Resource nets
E. NTS nets

Then list the advantages and disadvantages of each of the following net modes:
A. Voice
B. VHF Packet
C. HF Digital (such as AMTOR or PSK31)
D. CW

Appendix B (continued)

Learning Unit 7 Activity: Compose three complete ARRL/NTS formatted messages, one for each Precedence. Use Handling Instructions and include the time and date sent. To determine the word count for the check, refer to this link (http://www.arrl.org/FandES/ead/teacher/kemp/appendixa.html)

Learning Unit 8 Activities: Create a formal NTS style message using an ARL numbered radiogram text. Be sure the word count is correct.

Second,edit the following message text to reduce the number of words to a minimum, without losing any clarity.

"We need 50 additional cots and blankets at the Roe School shelter, and we also need more food since 20 new people just arrived and we are told another 30 may be coming soon. Please call me and tell me when these supplies will arrive."

Finally,go to the ARRL website and look up ARRL Numbered Radiograms:
http://www.arrl.org/FandS/field/forms/fsd3.pdf
When you have located the list of Numbered Radiograms, answer the questions that follow. Which of the Radiograms:
A. Indicates that a medical emergency exists?
B. Requests additional radio operators?
C. Offers congratulations on a new baby?
D. Offers greetings for a merry Christmas and happy New Year
E. Indicates safe arrival.

Appendix B (continued)

Learning Unit 9 Activities: 1. List the advantage and disadvantage of each of the following modes for an emcomm operation:

    A. Voice net

    B. CW net

    C. Packet

    D. Non-Packet Digital

What are the major topics found in ARRL's FSD-218?

Learning Unit 10 Activities: Outline a communication plan for a three-mile fun run on a straight course that will introduce or test an emcomm skill or procedure. Also in what ways would your three-mile fun run communication plan have to be modified for a 26 mile marathon?

Appendix B (continued)

Learning Unit 11 Activity: Contact a leader of your local emcomm group. Ask the leader:
    A. if the emcomm group is affiliated with a specific agency;
    B. if there is a local, planned ICS structure and if so;
    C. how the emcomm group fits into the local ICS structure.

Second, contact a leader of your local emcomm group. Ask the leader if the emcomm group has ever been activated. If so, what were the lessons learned from operating with local agencies?

Finally, suppose that during an emergency activation, you find yourself to be the leader of the local emcomm group. To which agency would you report? To whom within the agency would you report? What would your duties be as leader of the emcomm group?

Learning Unit 12 Activity: First create a jump kit list suitable for your area and assignment. Second, make a list of contacts and resources to keep in your jump kit

Appendix B (continued)

Learning Unit 13 Activity: Evaluate the equipment you now own to see if it is suitable for emcomm operation. Make a list of equipment you already own, and a second list of the items you will need to complete a basic emcomm package appropriate to your needs. Share the lists with your mentor.

Learning Unit 14 Activity: First list the strengths and weaknesses of the telephone tree as an alerting system. Second, list the strengths and weaknesses of paging as an alerting system. Then list the strengths and weaknesses of self-activation as an alerting system. Finally, design an emcomm activation system for a seven-member team. Be sure to include back up methods.

Appendix B (continued)

Learning Unit 15 Activities: Choose and complete two activities – share the results with your mentor.

1. Suppose that you were given the assignment of coaching a new member of your emcomm group. What six rules would you teach the new member regarding behavior at a served agency?

2. Within this lesson, the following statement was made: "Pack that equipment (radio gear) in your vehicle last so that you can get to it first." This is a concept that was developed during WWII, known as "combat loading."

Consider all the gear that you might need for a three-day emcomm assignment. How might you "combat load" your gear in a vehicle?

3. Develop a checklist of actions you should take upon arrival if you were assigned to a different served agency during an emcomm event.

4. Develop a checklist of actions you should take prior to departing a served agency at the conclusion of an emcomm event.

Learning Unit 16 Activity: Develop a set of "rules" to help a new emcomm group member deal with stress during an emergency. Second, develop a list of at least five possible served agency jobs that would also require your communication skills. Finally, develop five safety rules pertaining to generators and electrical lines in and near a radio room

Appendix B (continued)

Learning Unit 17 Activities: Do all of the following, and share the results with your mentor.
1. Prepare a disaster preparedness checklist specifically for your home and family.
2. Prepare a personal-needs checklist for yourself.
3. What are two major disaster threats in your area? For each threat, list five actions you would take as a precaution to protect your home and family.

Learning Unit 18 Activity: Choose and complete two, and share the results with your mentor.

1. Consider your own personal radio resources. Of the modes mentioned within this lesson, which would you consider acquiring for your own use? Why? Which would you not consider acquiring? Why not?

2. Select three of the digital modes. Identify the positive and negative aspects of using each of the three in an emcomm situation.

3. Based on the considerations you have identified above, develop a simple communication equipment plan for a small emcomm unit based in a small community. Within your plan, be sure to identify the equipment and modes you would employ.

4. How would the plan you developed above be different if your emcomm group were quite large and located in a large community?

Appendix B (continued)

Learning Unit 19 Activity: Choose and complete two activities. Share the results with your mentor.

1. Suggest some uses for alternate communication systems beyond those discussed here.

2. List the advantages and disadvantages for emcomm work of the following modes:
A. GMRS
B. FRS
C. CB
D. MURS

3. List the advantages and disadvantages for emcomm work of the following modes:
A. Cellular phones
B. Landlines
C. Couriers

Learning Unit 20 Activities: 1.Choose the next step you will take to either become involved with a local emcomm group, and/or the next step in your emcomm education. Share your choices with your mentor.

2. Suppose that you were placed in charge of training a new group of emcomm team members. To what five topics would you give the highest priority?